"You're not listening, Gary," I said patiently. "We're going back into Haiphong harbor, but we're not going to stay there for very long."

"Then how . . ."

"We're going to steal a gunboat tonight. When we have it, everyone is going to swim across and get on board, and then this ship is going to be started up, pointed straight for the harbor exit, and let go. Only there won't be anyone on board by then."

"In the confusion, we may be able to slip out of the harbor and make a run for the *Barracuda*," Sondra said.

Powell was looking from her to me and back again. "You're crazy," he said. He looked out at the distant gunboats again. "But there is no other way, is there?"

"None that I can think of," I said.

Powell seemed to think for a long time, until finally he nodded. "Let's do it then." He grinned. "The sonofabitches are in for the surprise of their lives."

NICK CARTER IS IT!

"Nick Carter out-Bonds James Bond."
—*Buffalo Evening News*

"Nick Carter is America's #1 espionage agent."
—*Variety*

"Nick Carter is razor-sharp suspense."
—*King Features*

"Nick Carter is extraordinarily big."
—*Bestsellers*

"Nick Carter has attracted an army of addicted readers . . . the books are fast, have plenty of action and just the right degree of sex . . . Nick Carter is the American James Bond, suave, sophisticated, a killer with both the ladies and the enemy."
—*The New York Times*

FROM THE NICK CARTER
KILLMASTER SERIES

Dedicated to the men of the
Secret Services of the
United States of America

A Killmaster Spy Chiller

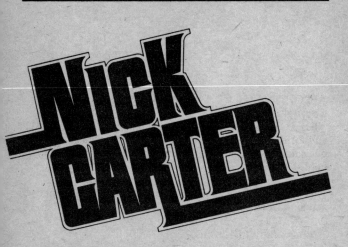

NICK CARTER

APPOINTMENT IN HAIPHONG

CHARTER
NEW YORK

A Division of Charter Communications Inc.
A GROSSET & DUNLAP COMPANY
51 Madison Avenue
New York, New York 10010

APPOINTMENT IN HAIPHONG

PROLOGUE

It was the rainy season and the man had been traveling through the jungle now for ten days. Moving only at night, sleeping in the trees with the spiders and snakes by day, and foraging for food as best he could, he had lost a lot of weight so that the skin hung in loose folds on his gaunt body. Leeches infested his legs, his sandals were nearly rotted off, and a fungus had attacked his feet leaving his toes little more than bloody stumps. Yet he continued. *Freedom*. The single thought ran round and round through his head. Freedom from fear, from hunger, from deprivation, from torture, both physical and psychological.

The night he had escaped from the camp he had made a mad dash across the border, hiding himself the first day about ten miles inside China.

He had seen the Chinese border patrol, but ten years of confinement in a jungle prison camp had honed his senses to an almost animal-like edge. He had easily slipped past them.

On the second and third nights he had continued traveling through China, parallel to the North Vietnam border, but on the fourth evening he had stumbled onto a Chinese border post that was heavily manned, and he had slipped back into Vietnam.

Each day his physical condition deteriorated a little more, but each day of freedom caused his spirit to soar, so that by the fifth day when he crawled up into a tree to rest, he resolved that he would not allow himself to be captured. He would die out here first. Die a free man.

It was two hundred miles to the Gulf of Tonkin, and despite the fact that the man often encountered villages with their outlying rice paddies, which he had to skirt, he managed to make nearly twenty miles a night.

On the tenth night, just before daybreak, he saw the lights of a large city on the horizon to the southeast.

He had climbed a tree, ready to settle down for the day, when he noticed the glow, and for several minutes he just stared at it wondering what exactly it was he was seeing. For a time he wondered if he had somehow gotten turned around and was seeing the lights on the guard towers back at the camp. But slowly he came to realize that he had almost made it.

The city to the southeast was Hanoi, fifty miles beyond which was the port city of Haiphong on the Gulf.

Three more nights at the most, and he would be at the gulf to the north of the city. Three more nights.

He slept heavily that day, although he kept hearing noises, like large animals growling and snarling not too far away.

The day was hot, although it was heavily overcast, and twice it rained, a torrential downpour that soaked the man to the skin despite the leafy protection overhead.

Still he slept. These conditions were normal for him. The strange noises were the only things bothersome.

But then, shortly before sunset when he was beginning to awaken, another sound startled him so badly he almost fell out of his perch. It was a sound he had not heard in more than ten years. A horn.

Below him, and less than twenty yards away, a large passenger bus had evidently broken down on a narrow, paved highway, blocking both lanes. A military truck that contained a dozen soldiers was stopped behind the bus, and the driver was blowing the horn.

The bus passengers had gotten out and were all shouting at the same time as an officer stepped down from the passenger side of the truck and pulled out his service revolver.

All day the man had slept in the tree, in plain sight of the highway. The animal sounds he thought he had heard had been the sounds of traffic. Anyone looking up would have seen him.

His heart was hammering nearly out of his chest as he carefully eased down to a lower branch, so that he was out of plain view from the highway, and then he dropped down to the jungle floor.

He crouched there behind the tree listening to the sounds of the argument out on the highway, waiting for the alarm to sound, and for the chase to begin.

But it didn't happen, and after a few minutes the man headed away from the highway, moving as silently as he could go.

It was another hour before full darkness. He was

very close to Hanoi, but he was weak and unarmed except for a six-inch-long piece of jagged metal, one edge of which he had sharpened by rubbing it against a rock back at the camp months ago.

Within a half an hour he had come to another highway, and he hid in the jungle until it was completely dark out. Then he made a dash across the road to the other side where he continued to the north, skirting Hanoi and its outlying communities.

Four more times he had to cross roads, and once around three in the morning he had come close to a small village where a dog, evidently sensing his presence, started barking.

The animal had either been tied up or penned, because he never appeared, and within a few minutes the man had left the barking far behind.

That morning the man made absolutely sure that the tree he selected for his hiding place was no where near a road or a village, then crawled up and went to sleep, spending a very uneasy day.

The next night was nearly a repeat of the previous evening's travel, but on the third night away from the highway, the lights of Hanoi long since lost far to the south, he came to a small fishing village on the coast.

He slept that day a few miles farther back in the jungle, and the next night a little after midnight slipped into the village, moving through the shadows down to the water's edge.

There were dozens of boats pulled up on the beach, a few of them with sails, and one of them with a large plastic jerry can, stamped U.S. Army, that contained water.

It took the man nearly an hour to move the

heavy wooden boat the twenty feet down to the water.

The wind was beginning to rise, and dark rain clouds began to move in as he finally launched the boat, set the ragged sail, and headed straight out to sea.

Freedom, he thought as the boat plowed through the mounting waves. He had made it through the jungle, but he suspected he would never make the sea voyage. It was more than five hundred miles across to the Philippines. An impossible distance. But he was free. He had beat them. He had escaped.

ONE

It was sometime after two in the morning when I finally gave up any attempt at sleeping, and I got out of bed. In the living room I poured myself a stiff shot of Remy Martin in a snifter, put on a record, and as the first booming crashes of Wagner's *Die Walküre* filled the room, I sat down and put my feet up.

Basically I am an operations man. I've always done my best work out in the field. But for the last few months I had been confined to AXE headquarters in the Amalgamated Press and Wire Services Building on Washington's Dupont Circle, running the Middle East Analysis Desk.

The situation there between Israel and Colonel Khadafy's Lybia was beginning to heat up, and from our best estimates this war, if it came, would be something more than a six day affair. Over the past months there had been a massive buildup of Soviet arms to the desert oil country.

In this instance, however, AXE had been warned to stay strictly in the intelligence gathering and analysis arena and remain totally out of the action.

That was fine with me. As far as I was concerned there was only one real solution to the entire situation, and that was the elimination of Khadafy. But despite his constant threats against our own leaders, we were told hands off.

The only problem was that I had been reduced these last months to nothing more than a glorified paper shuffler, and I was bored.

The door buzzer rang, and for just a moment, lost in the music, I thought the sound had come from the stereo speakers. But then the buzzer sounded again.

I put my drink down, got up and went to the intercom, and wondered who the hell could be here at this hour of the morning.

"Yes?" I said thumbing the button.

"Did I wake you, Nick?" a woman's voice came over the speaker.

"Who is it?"

"Sondra. Can I come up? It's lonely down here."

I hit the buzzer for the downstairs door, then opened my apartment door and stepped out into the corridor to wait for her.

Sondra Kinderman was my Middle East Operations Officer. It was her job to collate all the raw reports that came into headquarters, passing the digested material on to me.

If and when I felt that some kind of an operation had to be run in the region, I passed it back to her, and she pulled the proper strings to get it going.

She was very good at her job. She had come out of Vassar, one of the East Coast girls born with a silver spoon in her mouth, and although she definitely was a snob, she was an efficient snob.

Every man at headquarters had wanted to go out with her, but so far as any of us knew, her private life away from AXE was just that—private.

The elevator rose slowly from the ground floor, and the doors slid open. Sondra, wearing sandals, a pair of brief shorts, and a halter top, a bottle of champagne in one hand and two glasses in the other, stepped out into the corridor. When she saw me, she stopped and smiled. It looked as if she was slightly drunk.

"Hell of an outfit to be wearing around Washington, D.C. at this hour of the night," I said.

She laughed. "Is that a compliment or an admonishment, my dear Nicholas?"

"Christ," I said half under my breath. "Come inside and let me get dressed. I'll drive you home."

"Drive me home, bullshit," Sondra snapped, and she came down the corridor to me, holding the champagne up. "The first bottle was great, but I had to drink it alone. This one needs company."

When she reached me, she kissed my cheek, then brushed by me into my apartment. I followed her inside, closing and locking the door.

She put the glasses down on the coffee table, expertly opened the champagne and poured us both a drink. When she turned around, she had a bemused expression on her face.

"Surprised to see me?" she asked.

I nodded. "Very."

"I couldn't sleep. Thought I'd come over to see you."

I crossed the room to her and took my glass of champagne. "What are you really doing here?" I asked after I had taken a sip of the excellent wine. The girl did have good taste.

She held my eyes for just a second, but then she glanced over at the stereo. "Dreadful music for this time of night."

"I wasn't expecting company."

She looked back. There were tears in her eyes. "Don't send me home, Nicholas. Please."

"Did your boyfriend leave you?"

"You've been in my personnel jacket," she flared.

"Just a guess."

She listened to the music for a moment, then slowly kicked off her sandals and sat down on the couch, curling her legs up beneath her.

"I thought I could insulate myself from the office," she said distantly.

I sat down next to her.

"My parents love him. My brother thinks he's great. And he doesn't mind that I have my own career."

"But he's a bore?" I suggested.

She hung her head. "Christ, Nick, don't send me away. I've had all the rejection I think I can handle." Tears were welling up in her eyes.

I put my glass down, then took hers and set it on the table. She came into my arms immediately.

"Hold me . . . God, Nick, hold me," she cried.

For a long time we sat like that, in each other's arms, until her tears finally began to subside. I got up, helped her to her feet, and led her into my bedroom, where I gently undressed her.

I took my robe off as she slipped into bed, and then we were together, her body long, lithe, her breasts small, the nipples hard, and her lips and tongue all over me.

Twice during our lovemaking she called out her fiancé's name, Roger, and when we were finished she fell asleep in my arms, a troubled expression on her face.

I decided I would give her fiancé a call in the morning. I didn't think I'd accomplish much by it, but I at least wanted to tell him what a jerk he was.

I dropped Sondra off at her apartment around seven-thirty, then headed over to the Amalgamated Press and Wire Services Building, parking my car in the basement garage, and taking the elevator up to Operations.

The telephone in the glassed-in cubicle that served as my office, was ringing, and I picked it up before I took off my jacket.

"Operations. Carter."

"Nick, leave a note for Schmidt to take over the Mid-East desk, then get up here," David Hawk said, his tone particularly harsh this morning.

"Yes, sir." I hung up, jotted down a brief note for Smitty, then left it on his desk before taking the elevator up to the fifth floor where Hawk, AXE's director, maintained his office.

He was just coming out when I stepped off the elevator, and without a word we both got back on and rode down to the basement.

Hawk's black, bullet-proof limousine was waiting for us, and as we got off the elevator, his driver opened the rear door.

"Good morning, sir," the man said.

Hawk nodded, then climbed in the back seat. I got in next to him, the driver closed the door, hurried around to the front of the car, climbed in behind the wheel, and we headed out of the garage into the bright morning sun.

"What do you know about the MIA situation in Vietnam?" Hawk asked without preamble as we turned up Connecticut Avenue.

"I'd thought that was long since finished, sir," I said.

"So did I," Hawk said. He lit his cigar. "We all knew that there were probably a number of MIAs, most of them dead, that the Vietnamese government knows about. Every now and then an MIA pressure group gets Hanoi to release a body or two."

"But?" I prompted.

Hawk looked at me. He was a short man, ruggedly built, with a thick shock of white hair. No one in AXE knew his correct age, although we all guessed him to be in his early sixties.

"But no one has given much credence to the stories about MIAs as prisoners of war still being kept over there. Until now."

I looked at him. It was incredible. "Someone has come out of Vietnam? An American?"

Hawk was nodding. "U.S. Air Force Captain Robert Bruce. He was shot down in the Gulf of Tonkin in the spring of 1972."

"Good Lord. He's been a prisoner of war for ten years. Where was he held?"

"A number of places, but most recently in an internment camp near the Chinese border."

"Has his family been notified?"

Hawk turned away for a moment, then shook his head. "No, they haven't. Nor will they be for the moment."

"Why—" I started, but then clamped it off. There was more.

We had passed through Chevy Chase, and the driver turned on Jones Bridge Road, passing through the rear gate of the Bethesda National Naval Medical Center.

"Only a handful of people know that Captain Bruce is back, and it's going to remain that way for the simple reason that we don't want to jeopardize the others."

The idea was staggering. I was at a loss for words. The fighting in Vietnam had been over with for years. So why were they still holding American prisoners of war?

"How many others are there?" I asked.

Hawk looked at me. "According to Captain Bruce, the camp he had been held prisoner at contained one hundred and fifty POWs, some of them women."

"But why?" I asked. "What the hell have they got to gain by holding our people?"

The driver had pulled up to the rear entrance of one of the hospital buildings.

"I want you to see and talk with Captain Bruce first. I want your opinion. Then we'll decide what we're going to do."

I nodded. He and I got out of the car and entered the building. A guard was posted just inside, and we had to show some identification and sign in.

Captain Bruce's room was on the fourth floor. His doctor was just coming out as we stepped off the elevator and approached.

"How is he feeling this morning?" Hawk asked.

"Oh, good morning, David," the doctor said, looking up. He nodded at me. "He's doing much better today. By this afternoon he should be able to handle his first solid foods."

Hawk glanced toward the door. "Is he strong enough to see us?"

The doctor nodded. "But not for long. And I

don't want him to get overly excited."

"I understand," Hawk said. "Has he asked for his family yet?"

The doctor shook his head. "I have a feeling he'd just as soon have it this way. I don't think he wants to see anyone he knows until he regains his strength, and puts on a little weight."

Hawk and I entered the room, softly closing the door. The curtains were drawn, and except for a small night light in one corner, it would have been completely dark.

A thin, exceedingly emaciated figure lay on the bed, the covers up to his neck. His hair was cropped short, his eyes deeply sunken, and his cheeks hollow.

"Good morning, Captain," Hawk said softly, at the bedside.

Captain Bruce opened his eyes, looked up at Hawk and managed a smile. His teeth were all missing.

"Good morning," he croaked, his voice barely audible. He looked at me. "Is this him?"

Hawk nodded. "Nick Carter. He's the best there is."

Captain Bruce's gnarled right hand snaked out from beneath the covers, and he grabbed my wrist, his grip surprisingly strong. "You have to get them back, Carter, you must. Don't you see? Or they will die. They'll all die."

There was an odor of antiseptic and something else, something not so pleasant, coming from the man. How he had managed to escape was hard to comprehend.

I pulled a chair over and sat down near the head of the bed.

"Tell me, Captain Bruce, about the internment camp."

He was looking at me, his eyes blazing. "It's near Yen Minh, on the Chinese border," he started. "Ten, fifteen days on foot from the coast north of Hanoi."

"You went that far?"

A cackling sound came from his lips, and it took me a second or two to realize the man was laughing.

"Had to eat bugs and lizards. Other side of Hanoi I caught some rice paddy rats and ate them."

I looked up at Hawk.

"Captain Bruce walked from Yen Minh to the coast, where he stole a boat and sailed offshore during a monsoon storm. He was finally picked up fifty miles off the coast of Luzon in the Philippines."

I looked back at Captain Bruce. He was smiling, his eyes half closed.

"Never thought I'd make it," he said. "But it didn't matter. I kept thinking that I was a free man. Free!"

"Tell me about the camp," I said, leaning a little closer.

"There's one hundred and fifty of them left back there. Colonel Powell is senior officer."

"There are women there too?"

Captain Bruce's eyes blazed. "Six of them. Two are nuns. Thai Nong has used them . . ." He couldn't go on.

"Who is Thai Nong?" I asked.

"Lieutenant Colonel," Bruce said. "Bien Thai Nong. He's the camp commander. It was his idea to put dynamite under all the barracks huts. The switch is in his quarters. The entire place is set to blow."

The effort to talk seemed to wear him out, and his eyelids drooped, his voice a whisper.

"I knew the war was over," he said. "I figured I was alone. I thought I had been singled out for some reason to be kept behind. But there are one hundred and fifty others at Yen Minh. One hundred fifty."

Hawk motioned for me to leave, and I stood up, but remained by the bed for a few seconds. Bruce had fallen asleep, his thin chest rising and falling in a regular rhythm beneath the sheet.

Carefully I put his arm under the covers, then Hawk and I quietly left the room. We went down the corridor and took the elevator back to the first floor. We signed out with the security officer by the door, then, outside, climbed back into the waiting limo.

As we pulled away and headed for the back gate again, I glanced up at the window of Captain Bruce's room. The man's health would never return to normal. He would be underweight and sickly for the rest of his life.

"What do you think?" Hawk broke into my thoughts.

I turned and looked at him. "We've got to get them out of there."

"You believed him, then?"

"Why not?"

Hawk shrugged. "If Captain Bruce had been brainwashed into believing that the others existed, he would present a convincing story."

It was possible, I thought. "Is that what you believe?"

"No." Hawk shook his head. "No. He was able to give us the names of eighteen other POWs, which we checked with Department of Defense records. They're all legitimate names. All MIAs."

"How about the women?"

"He didn't know their names. But the commander, this Thai Nong character, he's legitimate as well."

"Have we got any other information on him?"

"Trained in Moscow. His specialty is interrogation."

"I see," I said. "His name alone makes Bruce's story more plausible."

"Either that, or his brainwashing more thorough."

I thought about that a moment. "Let's assume for a moment that Bruce's story is real. Why are they holding our people? What the hell do they have to gain this long after the war?"

"Reparation payments, for one," Hawk said, an edge to his voice. "Perhaps uncontested control of Laos, Cambodia, Thailand."

"We've heard nothing so far, have we?"

Hawk shook his head. "I suspect the political climate here isn't correct yet. They'll wait."

"A lot of those people could die in the meantime," I said.

"Some probably already have since their capture. But even if they only had one or two, think of their bargaining position. It'd be another Iranian hostage crisis all over again . . . only much worse."

We drove the rest of the way back in silence, the bright day seemingly less warm than before, and Sondra's problem certainly less important than it had been last night.

* * *

I spent the rest of the morning studying the tapes that were made of Captain Bruce's preliminary debriefing sessions. From the moment he had been picked up off the coast of Luzon, his comments had been recorded. Brainwashed or not, he presented a convincing story of his ten years imprisonment, and then his stunning escape.

After a quick lunch, Hawk called me back to his office where Sondra, along with Conrad Sternig, AXE's State Department Liaison officer, was waiting for me.

"Officially, the United States can't do a thing about it," Sternig said. "If Captain Bruce's escape was engineered by the Vietnamese, and his story nothing but brainwashing, we'd be playing directly into their hands by protesting.

"On the other hand, if Captain Bruce's escape was legitimate, and there are indeed one hundred and fifty POWs remaining there, we can't say a thing for fear that the Vietnamese will retaliate on the others."

"A difficult situation," Hawk said.

"Decidedly," the liaison man agreed. "But we do have one advantage."

We all waited.

"So far as we can determine, the Vietnamese believe that Captain Bruce perished at sea in the monsoon storm."

"So the Vietnamese believe their POW camp is still a secret from us," I said.

"Exactly," Sternig said. "But that may be a moot point. Political means certainly will not effect their release. The Vietnamese would simply deny their existence."

"Nor would a strike force," Sondra spoke up.

I looked at her, and she managed a weak smile. I was sure she was having second thoughts about what she had done last night.

"We can't be sure that the camp is actually booby trapped," I said. "Perhaps Captain Bruce and the others were merely told that."

"It doesn't matter," she said. "There are two factors operating here that make it impossible for us even to try. The first is the fact that our forces have made two attempts in recent years at dramatic rescue attempts. The first was in North Vietnam. The second was in Iran. In both instances, our plans did not work out. If we tried again, and failed, the U.S. public would crucify the President. Therefore such an attempt will not be allowed. And the second factor is the fact that Yen Minh is not only located right on the border of Communist China, it's also two hundred miles inland from the Tonkin Gulf. A hostile land, bordered by a hostile sea. We wouldn't have a chance of flying anything in there without detection."

"We can't leave them there," I said.

"No," Sondra said.

Sternig agreed. "Indeed, Mr. Carter."

Hawk was staring at me, a strange expression in his eyes.

"I'm to lead them out," I said.

Hawk nodded. "Something like that," he said. "You game?"

Sondra was staring wide-eyed at me, and Sternig had a slightly bemused expression on his face.

"Of course, sir," I said. "Have you got any ideas?"

"Some very specific ideas. But the chances for

your success will probably be less than one in ten."

I shrugged. "I've been on worse, sir."

Hawk stared at me for a long moment, but then he smiled. "Then we'll get started immediately."

"I'd like Sondra . . . Miss Kinderman, as my operations control officer," I said impulsively.

Hawk tried to hide his smile. "If you insist," he said.

TWO

It had taken us eight days in Washington, and another three days here in Brussels to get ready. Now that it was nearly time for me to leave, I was glad.

Captain Bruce had died two days ago. Complications because of his ordeal, Hawk had said. Heart difficulties, kidney failure . . . a host of problems.

Sitting across from Sondra now, at a table in our hotel dining room, I couldn't help but think of Captain Bruce's incredible journey on foot across more than two hundred miles of hostile territory, and then another five hundred miles across the sea in an open boat during a storm.

His death at this point was so damned senseless. It made me angry. Made me anxious to get started.

"It's too bad that he had to die like that," Sondra said, breaking into my thoughts.

I looked up. "Am I that transparent?"

"Sometimes," she said. "It's just that I don't want you to make any mistakes."

"I won't," I said after a moment. But she was right. If I thought too long and hard about Captain Bruce, I would be distracted. It was the worst possible thing that could happen to a field man out on assignment.

I signed for our dinner check, then Sondra and I had a couple of after dinner drinks at the bar before taking the elevator up to our floor.

During the last week and a half we had had no physical contact with each other. It was as if our lovemaking in my apartment had been a terrible mistake on her part, one that she was desperately trying to forget. Which was just as well, I kept telling myself. Sondra was an intelligent, highly efficient operations expert. My life would depend on many of the decisions she would be making while I was out in the field.

Now, during the planning and preparation stages, it was best that she too was kept free of distractions.

We stopped at her door. The corridor was deserted.

"What time are they expecting you?" she asked.

"Eight in the morning."

"We'll have to get up early then," she said. "I'll drive you out."

"When are you due in Naples?" I asked. She was wearing a frilly white blouse that did little to hide the swell of her breasts.

"Not until the weekend. I want to make sure that you're on your way."

"Fine," I said. "You've done a good job." I turned to go to my room.

"Nick?" Sondra said in a small voice.

I turned back.

"I don't want to be alone tonight," she said.

"You're sure?"

She nodded.

Nor did I want to be alone. She opened the door to her room, and we went inside where she came immediately into my arms, her lips searching for mine, her body shivering.

"Make love to me, Nicholas," she said. "Now . . . please."

We had parted, and she went over to the large bed where she turned back the covers, and then with shaking hands unzipped her skirt and stepped out of it.

I crossed the room to the phone on the night stand, called the hotel operator, and asked to be awakened here no later than six.

Sondra had pulled off her blouse and bra, and she was stepping out of her pantyhose now, her nipples hard, her entire body shivering.

The first time we had made love, there had been very little tenderness to it. It had mostly been a frantic coupling.

This time, I thought as I slowly began to undress, Sondra's eyes on my every move, we were going to do it my way.

Slow, gentle, and good.

We had made love most of the night, getting very little sleep, so that at six A.M., when the wakeup call came, I was tired. She had not called out her fiancé's name, like she had the last time, and now she slept with a smile on her face.

I got up, put on my slacks and shirt, and then carrying the rest of my clothes, left Sondra's room for my own. There was no reason for her to drive me out to the monastery this morning. I could make it on my own.

After a quick shower, I packed a few things in

my overnight bag, leaving the rest for Sondra to take care of, then went down to the breakfast bar off the lobby where I ordered a couple of croissants and a pot of black coffee.

Sondra would do all right. I had little or no doubt of it.

She would worry about me for a couple of days, but then as the operation progressed, and she became busy, she would concentrate on the job at hand.

I took my time over breakfast, reading the French language newspaper, and when I was finished I went through the lobby and outside where I had the doorman summon me a taxi.

After I climbed in the back seat of the cab, I glanced up at the upper floors of the hotel where Sondra still slept.

A lot was going to be happening over the next few weeks, none of it without extreme risk. The chances that I would succeed on this assignment and actually lead the one hundred and fifty American POWs safely out of Vietnam, were very small. Which is why Sondra and I had worked out a fail-safe over the past few days. No one knew about it. Not even David Hawk. But if worse came to worse, I would use it.

"*Monsieur?*" the cabby was asking.

I turned to him. "Do you know Tirlemont?"

"*Oui.*"

"The monastery there?"

His head bobbed up and down.

"Take me there," I said, glancing once again up at the hotel.

"It is forty kilometers."

I pulled some money out of my pocket and

handed several bills forward. "I must be there no later than eight."

"Yes, sir," the driver said crisply, his attitude much changed now that he had the money. He turned back to the steering wheel, flipped on the *occupied* sign, and we headed out of the city.

I lit a cigarette and settled back in the seat for the forty minute ride out of Brussels to the small town which contained a Catholic monastery that Hawk told me was several hundred years old.

It had been founded in the mid-1600s to in some way act as a countermeasure against the teachings of Calvin and the Reformation under Luther. Much later it evolved into an order of missionaries who traveled the world bringing help to oppressed people.

Gradually the monastic order of Tirlemont focused its efforts on the Far East, finally coming into contact with the Central Intelligence Agency at the beginning of the United States' involvement with the Vietnam conflict.

At first their help had been innocent: pinpointing which villages required their help, and others that didn't, because their support came from the Viet Cong.

But later, the monastery's field workers helped bring downed American pilots out of Vietnam, Laos, Cambodia and finally Thailand.

Although the North Vietnamese strongly suspected the Belgian priests of helping us, it had never been proven. And the day the American embassy in Saigon fell, was the day the monastery's aid ended.

"They were afraid of being totally ejected from

the region," Hawk had explained to me. "There's still work for them to do there, although they're confined now to Thailand."

"But they've agreed to help us now?" I had asked.

"Yes, but to a very limited extend, Nick. They will arrange to get you to Yen Minh, but at that point you'll be on your own."

"It's a start," I had said, and as we approached Tirlemont, the monastery came into view. It was perched on a solitary hill that rose out of the farm fields. At that moment I couldn't help but wonder what would be the outcome of this mission.

If the other one hundred and fifty POWs were in the same condition that Captain Bruce had been in, it would be nearly impossible to lead them on foot out of Vietnam, across Laos and finally into Thailand. Yet they could not be left there to die.

We passed through the town, and five minutes later we pulled up at the front gate of the monastery which was contained in the group of buildings behind a tall, stone wall.

The cabby jumped out and hurriedly opened the door for me.

"God bless, Father," he said as I went to the gate.

Before I rang the bell I turned around to look at him, but he had already gotten back into his cab and started down the hill.

He had naturally assumed I was a priest. Otherwise why come here. As I turned back and rang the bell at the large wooden door, I hoped that the Laotians and Vietnamese I would come in contact with, would think the same.

It took several minutes for someone to answer the door, and when it swung open a tiny, hooded figure was standing there.

"Nick Carter," I said.

The monk nodded, and without a word stepped aside to let me in.

A large, beautifully tended garden led up from the inner wall to the largest of the buildings about a hundred yards away. I followed the hooded figure along a stone path, and then into the four-story structure.

Just inside the door another hooded figure led me down a wide corridor with ornately carved wooden arches and beautifully done artwork making it seem like a museum.

At the end of the corridor the monk opened a door, stepped aside, and motioned me through.

An old man wearing a monk's garb, but with his hood thrown back, was seated behind a huge, leather-topped desk in front of French doors that opened onto another section of the garden. He rose when I came in.

"The American, Mr. Carter," he said, his voice soft. He had an odd accent—a mixture, I supposed of French and Flemish.

We shook hands. "Father Temse?" I asked.

He nodded. "Martin Temse. But I'm called Father Martin." He motioned toward a chair. "Won't you have a seat?"

When we were settled, he poured me a glass of light red wine. "And David Hawk is feeling well these days?"

"Yes," I said, "He asked me to convey my appreciation to you for your help."

The abbot waved it off. "We have not helped

yet, and I'm not so sure we can."

"I thought . . ."

"Oh, we will get you to Thailand, to Father Josef Van Der Woort, but I do not know if it will do you any good, young man."

I said nothing, waiting for him to continue.

"It is very dangerous for us at the moment in Laos. Two of our brothers have been missing for the past five days. There has been no word."

"The Pathet Lao?"

The abbot shrugged. "One can only guess at this stage." He sighed deeply, sat back in his thick chair and sipped at his wine.

"Was it explained to you, Father Martin, what I will be attempting to do?"

The priest nodded. "The intent is admirable, and yet one wonders if diplomatic means might not be less . . . shall we say . . . risky?"

"We've considered it," I said, setting my wine down. "But we believe that the Vietnamese government would delay any such negotiations, until they received certain concessions from my government."

"Concessions your government is not willing to grant."

"Not under the threat of hostages," I replied. "And meanwhile, during the negotiation procedure, many of those people would almost certainly die."

A look of sadness crossed the old priest's face. "I understand," he said tiredly. "It is the only reason why I have agreed to help. Although, as I have said, I'm not certain that we can be of much help."

He sat forward again, put his wine down and then got up. "But nothing will be accomplished here if we continue to chat like this and sip wine. Our next re-supply flight leaves Brussels Thursday morning, which gives us today and tomorrow to prepare you."

I got to my feet.

"You will be Herbert Karsten. Father Herbert, a novitiate missionary, on assignment to Father Josef Van der Woort."

He touched a button on his telephone console, and almost immediately a priest wearing a hooded robe came in.

"This will be Father Herbert. He is being assigned to Father Josef, so he will have to be made ready by Thursday morning."

The hooded priest nodded, then stepped aside for me to leave.

"Thank you again, Father Martin, for your help," I said, but the abbot had turned around to stare out at the garden, and he didn't seem to hear me.

I stepped out into the corridor, and a moment later the hooded priest led the way at a brisk pace back outside, then along another walk, to a long, low windowless building.

Just inside was a short counter, behind which stood another hooded priest who stared at me for several seconds, then turned and disappeared from view.

He was back a minute later, and he laid a pile of garments on the counter, which my guide picked up, then went through a doorway to the left.

I followed him down a narrow corridor that opened at the rear of the building to a large warehouse area, where at least two dozen robed priests, their hoods all thrown back, were loading clothing, food and what appeared to be medical supplies into large wooden crates. They worked in complete silence, each of them apparently knowing exactly what they were supposed to do.

We crossed the warehouse area and went through another door into a good-sized room that contained a low wooden cot, a table around which were four chairs, a blackboard, and an overstuffed bookcase along one wall. Along the opposite wall was a cabinet and an open door that led into a tiny bathroom.

When we were alone in the room, my guide pushed his hood back. He was a young man with broad features and wide, deep blue eyes. His hair had been cut to less than a quarter inch in length, but he was wearing a beard and mustache.

He stuck out his hand. "I'm Father Lars. Welcome to Tirlemont."

I shook his hand. "Pleased to meet you. I'm Nick Carter."

He shook his head. "No. You are Father Herbert. Do not forget it. Your life may depend upon it, from what I understand."

"You're right," I said. I glanced toward the closed door out to the warehouse. "I get the impression that this is a silent order."

"It is," Father Lars said, a slight smile at the corners of his mouth. "Only certain of us may speak, and then only in certain, designated areas and situations."

He laid the bundle of clothing on the table. "Are you hungry?"

"No, I've already had my breakfast."

"Lunch is at noon, dinner at eight. You will take your meals here, in this room. As a matter of fact, until we leave for the airport, you will remain in this room."

I nodded.

"Please change your clothing then, and we will begin."

I set my overnight bag down and began undressing, as Father Lars sat down in one of the chairs.

"What do you know of the history of our order?" he asked.

I told him what little I knew, but I didn't think he was really listening to me. Instead, his eyes had widened slightly when I unstrapped my Luger and then removed my stiletto in its chamois pouch on my left forearm. His eyes widened even more when I was completely undressed and he saw the tiny gas bomb I always carry in a specially designed pouch strapped high on my inner thigh, almost like a third testicle.

"It would give the communists quite a shock if they ever disrobed you," he said wryly.

I had to smile. "The shock would come if they tried, Father," I said, pulling on the robes and slipping into the pair of sandals I had been issued.

He got up, pulled the chair around, and motioned me to it. "Sit down, and please say nothing while the barber is here."

I did as he asked, and when I was seated, he went to the door, opened it, and another robed priest entered.

A towel was placed around my neck, and quickly and very efficiently the barber-priest cut my hair, leaving nothing on my head but a very short stubble.

When he was finished, he cleaned up the hair

from the floor, bundled up his clippers and scissors, and left without a word.

"Welcome to the Order of Tirlemont," Father Lars said, grinning.

"I don't suppose there's a mirror in the place?"

"Not one. It would be considered vanity," he said. "Besides, you wouldn't want to see yourself now."

I laughed out loud, rubbing a hand over my nearly bald head.

"So," Father Lars said, sitting down across the table from me. "Let us begin. You have much to learn, and there is so little time."

Father Lars had been right. There was a lot to learn and very little time in which to learn it. At first I had chafed at the tremendous amount of historical detail I was being given. But after a time it became apparent that every single thing the priests of this order did and thought, had precedent in the history not only of their order, but of the Mother Church.

At one point, late on Wednesday night, Father Lars had left my room, returning a few minutes later with a bottle of brandy, two glasses, and a package of American cigarettes.

He poured us a drink as I lit a cigarette.

"I think you are beginning to understand now, that it takes a lifetime to learn to be a priest in this order," he said.

My stomach rumbled, and my eyes burned.

"All that before we begin to do any work," he said. He looked away momentarily. "I think you should understand that I believe what this order

has done over the past fifteen years has been dread-
fully wrong."

"Your involvement with us in Vietnam?"

He looked back and nodded. "Yes. And this
now, with you."

"Good people will die without our help."

"And when you are finished and have gone, other good people will die instead."

"Not if I can help it," I said.

"You cannot," the priest said with feeling. "But
so be it. We each have our own burdens."

I had finished my drink, and he poured me another. "Shall we continue?"

"What time do we leave in the morning?"

"The plane is scheduled to take off at seven.
We'll have to be there and begin to load it no later
than four."

I looked at my watch; it was nearly midnight.
"We have only a couple of hours left then, before
we have to leave. Let's finish up."

"We are finished," the priest said. "You have
learned all I can teach you in such a short time."

I felt as if I knew nothing about the order. "How
closely are your people . . . are we, watched over
there?"

"Very," he said.

"Then how will I be able to pull it off?"

He managed a slight smile. "There *is* one thing
left for you to learn. The most important precept of
being a priest in this order. Know it well, and you
will know all there is to know about us."

I said nothing, waiting for him to continue.

"But for a man in your position . . . for a man of
your vocation, what I am about to tell you may

well be totally impossible for you to grasp, let alone use."

Still I held my silence.

"Love your enemy," he said softly.

I had half expected it. "Turn the other cheek and all that?"

Father Lars nodded. "At a deeper level, Mr. Carter, you must have an understanding of the human condition. All of us are God's children. All of us are His creation."

"Even those who murdered Captain Bruce?"

"Even them. Especially them. They need our help the most."

"Then you would advocate me not going ahead with my mission?"

"Precisely," he said, and he got up. "But in this *you* are the enemy to my order, yet I can understand, and still feel love in my heart for you."

I sighed deeply. "Wish me luck then."

He shook his head. "What will be done, will. It is His domain."

THREE

Bangkok and its environs is a city of two million people, most of them incredibly poor by Western standards. The bulk of Far Eastern humanity pressed in on us as harshly as the tremendous heat and humidity as we stepped off the plane at the international airport northwest of the city.

Beggars were everywhere, many of them maimed or crippled; all of them were obviously in the throes of starvation.

In the lee of the relatively modern, well constructed airport terminal, were straw and corrugated iron shacks, containing several generations.

Toward the center of the city, along the Chao Phraya River and the many fetid canals that cut the city in sections, people were compressed in crude waterfront shacks or aboard flimsy river craft.

The streets were filthy, the buildings grimy, and the air thick with a haze, rich in undefinable odors.

I had been to the Far East on several occasions. But each time I left I forgot just what it was like here. Each time I returned it was a rude awakening.

"Man's inhumanity to man," Father Lars said softly at my elbow.

I turned to look at him. "It must be difficult to turn the other cheek in a place like this," I said, instantly regretting the cheap shot.

But the priest nodded. "Very," he said. "Which is one of the reasons we are here, Father."

"Sorry," I mumbled, and I followed him back to the plane's open cargo doors as the Thai customs authorities came out to us.

The customs officer was a short, weasel of a man accompanied by a dozen armed soldiers.

He checked our papers first, including the papers of the pilot and copilot, then took Father Lars aside behind the aircraft.

While the rest of us waited, the soldiers stood watching us.

A couple of minutes later Father Lars and the now broadly grinning customs agent, returned to us. The agent stamped our papers, as well as the aircraft's cargo documents, and then got back in his jeep and took off with his soldiers.

"What happened back there?" I asked Father Lars.

"Dash," he said.

I had suspected as much. "How much did you have to pay him?"

"One third of the value of our cargo."

"That's a little steep, isn't it?"

Father Lars nodded. "I didn't want to risk having him check your papers too closely."

Two canvas covered trucks came from the terminal area, their drivers hooded priests like us. The first truck was backed up to the aircraft, and Father Lars and I, along with the other three priests who had traveled with us from Belgium, as well as the two drivers, began moving the supplies.

It only took about forty-five minutes to load both trucks, but by then it was nearly noon, and the fierce sun was almost directly overhead.

It was at least one hundred degrees with the humidity to match, and by the time we were finished, my robes were plastered to my body.

"Wouldn't shorts, a T-shirt and a coolie hat make more sense in this climate?" I asked.

"You'll get used to it," Father Lars said.

We climbed aboard the trucks, Father Lars and I riding together in the front of the lead truck, and the others in the back with the cargo. When we were all aboard we headed away from the airport.

We skirted north of the city, and within half an hour were making good time north along a wide, well-maintained highway.

"This is the main north-south military road," Father Lars shouted over the noise of the truck engine.

"How close to Chiang Khan will it take us?" I asked.

"About fifty or sixty miles," he said. "This road actually connects with Vientiane. But the border is closed now, and the highway just ends."

We were traveling now through rice country, and for as far as the eye could see, were rice paddies with workers up to their knees in the rich, black mud.

From time to time we would pass through a cluster of crude, thatched huts, and then we would be back out in the countryside.

I had not been told very much about Father Josef Van der Woort, except that he ran the Order's leper colony located on the Laotian border just outside the town of Chiang Khan.

The man was a Belgian medical doctor and something of an odd, independent duck from what the abbot and Father Lars had told me.

He had not been informed of my mission, and although I felt there was a possibility he would refuse to help, Father Martin had not thought it likely.

"Besides his work at the mission, Father Josef loves a good fight above all else," the abbot had told me.

"You think he will agree to take me into Vietnam?" I asked.

"Certainly. He is a raging anti-communist. He hates them and what they have been doing in that part of the world." Father Martin had summoned me to his office a few minutes before we had left for the airport in Brussels. He sat forward now. "But I will caution you on one point, Father Herbert."

I waited.

"Beyond guiding you to Yen Minh, Father Josef will *not* become involved." The abbot looked pointedly at me. "Instructions, explicit instructions to that effect will be sent along."

"How about transportation?"

"That is within Father Josef's domain." The abbot looked away momentarily. "Sitting here, safe and comfortable, I cannot imagine how your mission will succeed. But it is not for me to say. It is for you, and you alone. I do wish you luck."

Luck I thought now riding in the truck. Here they would call it joss . . . which translated more accurately to fate.

We stopped around six, just outside the village of Lom Sak, for a meal of hard rolls, weak tea and a very good soup that the priests heated on a charcoal fire at the side of the road.

It was a silent meal, made doubly strange by the oppressive heat and humidity of the evening.

By six-thirty we were back on the road which finally turned northeast two hours later. Our driver slowed way down and pulled the truck into low gear until we finally turned off the well paved highway onto a dirt track that was little more than a heavily rutted path through the jungle.

"Fifty miles of this?" I shouted over the noise.

Father Lars managed a smile. "No," he shouted. "The road gets much worse farther on."

Sometime around eleven P.M., we passed through the small town of Loei, and for a few miles the dirt road had been graded and provided fairly easy passage, but then it narrowed again, and we had to slow to less than fifteen miles per hour.

In spots, logs had been laid down along sinkholes so that vehicles would not get stuck. At other spots the path was so narrow that tree branches scraped both sides of the trucks.

A few minutes after midnight we came around a sharp bend and had to pull up short. Two jeeps and a military truck equipped with machine guns, blocked our way. A spotlight was shined on us, making it impossible to see anything outside.

"What is this?" I asked.

"I don't know," Father Lars said. "Nothing like this has happened before."

I reached for my Luger, but he stayed my hand. "That won't do us any good," he snapped. "Stay here, I'll see what the trouble is. But whatever you do, don't say a thing, and don't try to fight your way out."

He got out of the truck and went forward. A Thai officer and three armed soldiers met Father Lars just at the hood of our truck.

They argued there for a minute or two, until they all came back, demanding my papers and the papers of our driver.

We handed them over, a flashlight was shined on our faces, and a moment later our papers were tossed up in the cab.

Father Lars and the soldiers went to the back of the truck, and I could hear them shoving boxes and crates around back there.

"What's happening back there?" I asked the driver.

He just shook his head, but said nothing.

It took them at least fifteen minutes before they all came back around the front, and this time the officer and soldiers were carrying boxes of what appeared to be medical supplies.

Father Lars climbed back up in the cab with us, but motioned for me to keep silent for the moment.

A couple of minutes later the spotlight was doused, the jeeps and trucks backed up the path, and then off to a wide spot, allowing us to pass.

They watched us as we drove slowly by.

"What happened?" I asked. "Why did they stop us?"

Father Lars was angry. I could see it in his eyes and in the set of his jaw.

"They apparently found out that we were bringing in a larger quantity of medical supplies than usual."

"More dash?"

He nodded. "Almost all of our morphine."

"What will Father Josef do without it?"

"Do?" Father Lars snapped. "Endure. Like always."

Love thine enemy. The words repeated themselves in my brain. A noble idea, but one almost impossible to live with in the real world.

It was well after one in the morning when we finally came into the Order's leper colony. We were all bone weary, so the lights that shone from several of the low, crudely constructed buildings, were a welcome sight.

Our driver pulled through the compound's open gate, then swung around and parked in front of the largest of the buildings.

He doused the headlights and switched off the engine, and as I was climbing down out of the truck, a huge bear of a man barged out of the big building. He wore sandals and a pair of tan shorts, but nothing on his back. His thick black hair was down to his shoulders, and his beard and mustache had probably never been trimmed.

"Shit and damn, where the hell have you people been?" he bellowed as he came across to us.

I stepped aside as Father Lars, who had been talking to our driver, turned around. "We came in late, and we were stopped on the road less than thirty kilometers away from here."

"The dirty bastards," the giant of a man said. Standing next to him I felt like a midget. "I suppose they got the morphine."

Father Lars nodded. "Most of it."

"Goddamn them," the man swore softly. "God, send the heathens to hell."

Father Lars smiled sadly. He turned to me.

"Father Herbert, I'd like you to meet Father Josef."

I almost looked beyond the big man to see if there was someone else there before I realized that he was Father Josef. The surprise must have been evident.

Father Josef laughed, throwing his head back, the sound coming from deep inside. When he recovered he looked me up and down. "This a silent one, or one who can speak?"

"I can talk," I said. "I've come to ask for your help."

Father Josef's eyes narrowed. He glanced at Father Lars. "He's not one of the Order?"

Father Lars shook his head, then handed across a thick manila envelope. "Father Martin has included some special instructions."

Father Josef took the envelope, but made no move to open it.

"You're an American?"

I nodded.

"CIA?"

"No."

"But you're with one of the intelligence services?"

"Yes."

He seemed to think a moment. "It's not Thailand you'd be interested in. Nor would it be Cambodia. You're at the wrong end of the country for it. Which leaves Laos, Vietnam or China. Which?"

"Vietnam," I said softly.

"Shit," he said. Out of the corner of my eye I could see Father Lars wincing.

The other priests had begun unloading the

trucks and bringing the supplies into the big building.

"Let me guess. You're here to release POWs."

Again the surprise must have been evident on my face, but this time Father Josef did not laugh.

"I thought as much." He looked at Father Lars. "Is this going to be a private war, Lars, or are you and the others going to be in on it?"

"That's up to you."

"Fine. You can take over the facility. Can't leave it run on its own. They'd rob us blind . . . those of them who didn't die without help."

Father Lars started to say something, but Father Josef motioned for me to come along, and he turned on his heel and stalked back up to the main building.

I hesitated.

"Go ahead," Father Lars said. "We'll unload the supplies."

"Thanks for your help."

Father Lars started to turn away, but then turned back. He stuck out his hand. "Good luck."

I shook it. "Thanks, I think I'm going to need it," I said, and I went into the building, which turned out to be a large, fairly well equipped dispensary.

Light shone from an open door at the rear of the room, and I crossed over to it, knocked once on the doorframe, and stepped inside what appeared to be a small apartment.

"Close the door," Father Josef called from one of the other rooms. "And smoke 'em if you got 'em."

I went to an open window where a very soft breeze was blowing and lit myself a cigarette. Laos was just a couple of miles north of here, across the Mekong River. Once we crossed that border we would be in enemy territory. If I was captured alive, it would be a disaster not only for the POWs in Vietnam, but for AXE as well.

"How do you want to be called?" Father Josef asked from behind me.

I turned around. He had come from the other room carrying a tray with a bottle of cognac, a couple of glasses, and several bowls of steaming food.

"Father Herbert," I said.

Father Josef set the tray down on the table and motioned me over, and then sat down himself. "I imagine you're hungry. Have something to eat, and we'll talk."

I joined him at the table. The food turned out to be a very good combination of steamed rice, vegetables and several varieties of meat.

We ate in silence, and when we were finally finished, Father Josef poured us both a healthy measure of the cognac. He lit himself a cigar, and then sat back in his chair and belched loudly.

"Go ahead and ask me," he said.

"For help?"

"We'll get to that," he said impatiently. "I meant about how I knew about the American POWs at Yen Minh."

"How did you know?"

"Shit, everyone here knows about it."

"We didn't."

Father Josef shook his head. "You Americans never learn do you?" He took a deep drink of his liquor, then poured himself more. "In all fairness, the French were no better in the fifties. But at least they had the sense to give it up before it got too bad. You people had to back yourselves so badly into a corner, that the entire world was laughing at you." He sat forward. "Even now you won't listen to what's really happening out here. Hell, I'm sure that your people have accurate MIA lists. Isn't it logical to assume that not *all* of them are dead? Isn't it logical that some of them are still being held as prisoners?"

"Can you take me to Yen Minh?" I asked.

He looked at me for several seconds. "How did you find out about it?"

"One of our people managed to escape."

"I'll be damned," Father Josef said, genuinely surprised. "Haven't heard a rumble about that one. How?"

"On foot to a fishing village north of Haiphong, and from there by open boat to Luzon."

"The man had *cajones*. How's he doing?"

"He died."

The bluster seemed to go out of the burly priest, his eyes suddenly moist. "He died a free man."

"I want the others free as well," I said.

"Two of our nuns are there. Did you know that?"

I nodded. "Will you take me to Yen Minh?"

"What have you got in mind once you get there?" he asked, ignoring my question for the moment.

"Bring them back the same way we came."

"Bullshit," the priest shouted, thumping his fist on the table. "How many prisoners are there—any idea?"

"One hundred and fifty."

He nodded. "And you expect to waltz back across Vietnam, and then Laos with them? Some of them probably crippled. Not one of them with more strength than a child."

I said nothing.

"It'd take two weeks with that mob. How would you feed them?"

"Will you take me to Yen Minh?"

Father Josef bit back a sharp reply. Instead he stared at me for several long seconds. Finally he sat forward, poured me another drink, and himself a third, then sat back.

"I'll take you to Yen Minh," he said. "And it looks as if I'm going to have to lead you and your people back here by the hand."

"Your abbot, I believe, has sent you instructions to the contrary."

"What instructions?"

"They are in the manila envelope that Father Lars handed to you."

"Hell of a thing about that damned envelope," he said smiling. "I had it just a minute ago, but before I could open it, I set it down. Be damned if I can remember now where I put it."

I drank my cognac and lit myself another cigarette as I debated passing up his offer. The chances that I would be able to lead the POWs back through Vietnam and Laos by myself were almost nil. The fail-safe that Sondra and I had worked out, was just that, nothing more than a fail-safe that I would try only if all else failed and our backs were totally against the wall.

Father Josef, on the other hand, had lived and worked in this part of the world for all of his adult life. If anyone could raise our odds of coming back out, it would be him.

"Tell me about conditions these days in Laos and Nam," I said.

Father Josef smiled. "There just may be some

modicum of sense in that shaved skull of yours,"
he said. He jumped up, went to his desk, rummaged around in one of the drawers and came
back with a large, well-used map showing everything from Vietnam in the east to Burma in the
west.

"Getting there is going to be the difficult part, as
far as our stamina is concerned," he said, spread-
ing the map out on the floor.

I got down with him, both of us on our hands
and knees. "I assume we'll be going up the Mekong
River."

"Part of the way," he said, tracing a blunt finger
along the wide, meandering river. "But halfway
through Laos, at Luang Prabang, we'll have to go
overland. It's just too big a city to risk a river passage through it. Probably contains ten or twelve
thousand people. There's also a military garrison
there."

"Where do we cross the border?"

"Much farther north," Father Josef said. "Up
here, near Muong Va. There's been some new road
construction out there recently. We'll parallel it,
right along the Chinese border."

I looked at him. "How do you know about the
road construction."

Father Josef managed another smile. "It's this
way, Father Herbert, The Thai people aren't the
only ones who get ill. Laotians, and even Vietnamese are prone to it as well. And they do need help."

"How long will it take us to get to Yen Minh?"
I asked.

"If we're lucky? Perhaps ten days."

"Damn," I said. "No other way?"

"Not if we want to keep our arrival at Yen Minh

a secret," he said. "We'll be coming back a hell of a lot faster."

"What have you got in mind?"

"You have to understand that authority, military authority, in Laos is chaotic at the moment. Anyone in an officer's uniform can pretty well do as he pleases."

I was suddenly beginning to understand. "We bring them out in a military convoy."

"Exactly," he said.

"That's across Laos. What about Vietnam itself?"

"You weren't listening," Father Josef said. "In Vietnam, we'll be a Vietnamese convoy. In Laos, a Laotian convoy."

"And if we're stopped?"

"We're going after fighting men. Given weapons, I think they might be willing to use them. And every mile we travel by truck, will be one less mile the poor bastards will have to walk."

FOUR

We hid in the thick undergrowth on the Thailand side of the Mekong River. Several hundred yards across was a Laotian border patrol that had stopped at the water's edge. A spotlight searched the dark stretches of river for several minutes. Finally it was doused, and the patrol moved off.

Father Josef, who had been intently studying the far shore through a set of binoculars, turned back to us.

"Once again, Father Lars, I'm going to ask you to remain behind. There is no reason for you to come along."

It had taken us two days to get ready for the penetration of Laos and then Vietnam, and during that time Father Lars had gone about the business of getting his assistants ready to take over the leper colony. This afternoon he had surprised us with his announcement that he would be coming along.

He wasn't going to be talked out of it now.

"I have my instructions," Father Lars said. "Which you would understand had you read yours."

"I could just leave you here."

"I think not," Father Lars said, and he turned to me. "How about you?"

"Do you think, Father, that you could shoot someone if need be?"

He shook his head.

"Then you should remain behind," I said.

Father Josef came back to us. "I don't want to be a disappointment to you, Father Herbert, but I'm not going to shoot anyone either. If it has to be done, you'll have to do it. For all my bluster, I am a priest."

I groaned inwardly, although I guess I wasn't really surprised.

"It still leaves us you, Father Lars. Are you intent on tagging along?"

"I am."

"Then so be it," Father Josef said. "Let's get at it. We have a long way to go."

The three of us dragged the large canvas-covered canoe that contained our supplies down to the water's edge, and shoved it in. I took the bow, Father Lars climbed in the middle, and Father Josef shoved us off, stepping nimbly into the rear seat.

The current started to swing the bow out into the middle, and I had to work hard for several minutes to bring it back toward shore. We were traveling upriver, and the current in the middle would be too stiff for us to make any headway. In addition we would be dangerously exposed to view. For the first miles we would remain close to the west shore. Later, Father Josef had told us, we would cross over to the east shore and continue to within ten miles of Luang Prabang, where once again we would cross back to the west side. There we would hide the canoe and continue overland on foot.

If all went well we would be at Yen Minh within

ten days, traveling only at night, and hiding in the jungle during the daylight hours.

The first hour was difficult, a deep ache settling into my back and my shoulder muscles. But gradually I fell into a smooth, comfortable rhythm, and mile by mile we silently worked our way deeper into Laos, the evening warm and humid, the night insects voracious, and the jungle always pressing in on us.

Around one A.M., Father Lars and I switched positions, and while he rowed for an hour, I drank some water and ate cold C rations.

At two o'clock Father Lars took over for Father Josef, allowing The Bear, as I learned his nickname was, to eat and rest.

Through the night we continued to push up river, finally stopping around five-thirty as the sky to the east began to lighten.

We had just managed to push the long canoe into a tangle of branches and other flotsam that had been snagged along the shoreline, when the sound of a powerful motor came from upriver.

Father Josef quickly pulled more branches around us and then motioned for us to duck low.

Within a few seconds the sound of the motor was right on top of us, and through the branches we could see a Laotian gunboat pass us in midriver.

For a long time we could hear the motor sound downriver, but finally it was lost to the distance and we sat up.

"You and Father Lars sleep now," Father Josef said softly. "I'll take the first watch."

"Four hours each?" I asked.

"Sure," Father Josef said. Father Lars had already lain down.

"It won't do to get run down, Father," I said.

He grinned. "I needed the exercise," he said. "Now get some sleep, or tonight you'll be sorry you didn't."

I had to smile as I lay back against the packs, but I was instantly asleep.

When I awoke the sun was a bright red orb in the west, and it was incredibly hot. I was drenched with sweat, and my muscles ached as I sat up and looked aft.

Father Josef, a slight smile on his lips, a rosary entwined in his fingers, sat erect. He was praying.

I averted my gaze as I stretched.

"You had a pleasant sleep?" he said softly.

I turned back, "I didn't mean to disturb you, Father."

He smiled. "You're confused about me, aren't you?"

I nodded.

His smile broadened. "So is Father Lars," he said. The other priest was still sleeping. "But the abbot and I understand each other. We go a long way back together."

"What are you doing here?" I asked.

"Here in the Far East? Or here on this river with you?"

"Both," I said.

He thought a moment. "Well, we have the next week and a half. Perhaps I can explain myself in that length of time, although I doubt it. I don't understand it myself, except that I'm serving my Lord, Jesus Christ. Here? America? Europe? It really doesn't matter."

"Why the bluster?"

Father Josef chuckled. "The meek may inherit the Earth, but they won't all be priests."

Father Lars began to wake up, and Father Josef glanced down at him.

"Don't be so hard on him," he said. "He is a good man."

I nodded.

"He's just different from us," Father Josef said. Then he brightened. "You ever play soccer?"

"A little," I said. "But never seriously."

"That's all right. I'll tell you about my sports days. Maybe you'll understand me a bit better." He laughed. "I was one hell of a player in my day."

We waited until it was completely dark before we pushed off and continued upriver. Within half an hour my muscles had loosened up, and I dug in to a deep, steady rhythm. Yesterday we had only made thirty-five miles; tonight we were pushing for fifty.

Four times we had to pull into the undergrowth to avoid passing gunboats; yet when we finally stopped around five-thirty, Father Josef figured we had nearly made our fifty miles.

I took the first watch while the other two slept. We were tied up about twenty yards from the main channel, and all through the morning the river was busy with traffic.

Every now and then I could hear the powerful motor of a gunboat patrolling the river, and from time to time I caught glimpses of large, flat-bottomed boats being poled up river by men wearing only loincloths.

At ten I woke Father Lars, and he took over while I slept.

By nine P.M., when it was dark again, we were all rested, but very stiff as we paddled out to the river and continued upstream.

Father Josef figured that by morning we would be just below the capital city of Luang Prabang, so this evening was our last night on the river.

During the rowing none of us spoke. Sound carried too well across the water, and from time to time we passed within yards of settlement docks along the shore.

The closer we came to Luang Prabang, the more riverside settlements there were, the more gunboats there were patrolling, and the more flotsam and other garbage there was floating.

Still, we continued on, and I began to get the impression that Father Josef was looking for something along the opposite shore.

It was around four in the morning when we finally stopped and he pointed across the river with a dripping paddle.

"We cross here," he said softly.

"What about the patrol boats?" Father Lars asked.

"We wait until one passes, and then we go," Father Josef said, and I nodded.

The river was about three hundred yards across here, and the night was pitch black so that I couldn't see a thing on the other side. All during this trip, so far, Father Josef had displayed an intimate knowledge of the river. There was no doubt left in my mind that he had traveled this way many times before.

We had pulled close into the shore and were holding on to overhanging branches so that we would not drift downstream.

About fifteen minutes after we had stopped I turned to ask Father Josef what was across the river, when we all heard the sound of an approaching gunboat, and we instinctively hunched farther down in the long canoe.

The boat was coming slowly upriver, its spotlight flashing along the opposite shoreline. A few minutes later it passed directly across from us, and within five minutes it was gone.

"Now," Father Josef whispered urgently.

We let go of the branches, turned toward midstream, and dug in, paddling as hard and as fast as we possibly could go.

The current was much stronger than I thought it would be, and despite our best efforts we were being swept far downstream, and we redoubled our efforts.

Just beyond the midway point, we heard the sound of the gunboat upriver from us, and we all turned to look that way as it came into view, its spotlight continuing to search the shoreline.

"Move, move! Put your muscle into it!" Father Josef snapped.

The wide canoe paddle bit deeply into the dark water, and I put every ounce of my strength into each stroke.

We were rapidly approaching the opposite shore, and I could see a narrow channel just below us. But the sound of the gunboat's engine was loud now, drowning out all other sounds, and out of the corner of my eyes I could see the bright flashes of its spotlight.

I bent even harder into the task, and I could feel Father Josef's powerful strokes in sync with my own, pushing up the last few yards.

Then we shot into the narrow channel, pulled up our paddles and ducked low, as the gunboat passed directly behind us, the beam of the spotlight flashing just overhead. Then it was gone, and I let out a deep sigh.

"That was close," Father Lars said.

"Too damned close," Father Josef agreed softly. "But we can't stay here." He looked at his watch. "We have about an hour to get clear of the city. We'll have to move fast."

We paddled another twenty yards down the narrow channel before we pulled up and went ashore, the first solid land under our feet in three days.

When we had all the equipment out of the canoe, Father Josef pulled out a long, razor-sharp machete and quickly sliced two large gashes in the bottom of the boat. Then he shoved it out to the middle of the channel, and it began to fill with water.

Within a couple of seconds the canoe had sunk out of sight, leaving only a few bubbles in its wake.

The food, clothing and medical supplies we had brought with us were distributed evenly in three packs, each weighing around sixty pounds.

When we were dressed in the monk's habits, and had hefted the packs, we started off at a very brisk pace, Father Josef in the lead. If we were stopped from this point on, we would be monks from the Order's leper colony at Chiang Khan on our way north to help anyone who needed us.

It was a flimsy cover, one that would be blown if I was searched, but it was the best we had.

The only weapons we carried, besides my own, were the machetes used to cut a path whenever the undergrowth became too dense. It was unsettling to be so deeply into enemy territory and so lightly armed, in addition to being with two men who would not fight, but would offer only passive resistance.

Yet, without Father Josef as a guide, I probably would have never gotten this far.

The sky was bright enough with the rising dawn, so that we could see through the woods we were traveling in; and this is how we spotted the burned-out village.

We stopped at the edge of the clearing and watched for a few minutes. Rising above the trees to the west was a thin wisp of smoke.

"This place was burned out during the war," Father Josef explained. "The rebuilt village is about a mile west."

"The smoke?" I asked softly.

He nodded. "They probably won't be coming here, but we'll post a watch just the same."

"You've been here before?" Father Lars asked, looking from the village remains, to Father Josef.

The big priest nodded, a strange look coming into his eyes. "There were many burn victims here. Napalm, mostly. And most of them were beyond help." He looked again at the rough collection of huts, most of them little more than charred rubble. "I can still hear the children screaming."

We held our silence for a long moment, until Father Josef shook himself out of his remembrances. Suddenly he crossed the clearing and entered one of the crude huts still perched on its supports, which held the floor about three feet above the constantly damp ground. We followed when he gave us the all clear.

After we ate a quick meal, Father Lars lay down

and fell instantly asleep. It was to be my watch, but Father Josef didn't seem able to settle down.

"You should get your rest," I said gently.

He just looked at me.

"We have another seven days of this . . ." I began.

"Christ, it's so futile," he interrupted. "We'll release your soldiers, and in doing so there will be deaths."

I nodded. "If we do nothing, if we turn around now and go back, there will be deaths as well. Many of our people will die in that prison."

"I know," he said. "Which brings us down to a choice of who will die." He passed a hand over his forehead. "For you the choice is simple. You are a soldier, the Vietnamese your enemy. You are on a mission of mercy."

"And for you?"

"I don't like playing God . . . having to choose who will live and who will die. He's having enough trouble with the job Himself, without my interference."

"You're just guiding me to Yen Minh," I said, by way of consolation.

"Shit," Father Josef swore. "You and I both know better than that. I'll get your people out of there." He shook his head. "I'm a paradox. Father Martin undoubtedly told you that I love a good fight. And I do. So I will help your people get their freedom. But I don't like death. So if there is any possibility, however slight, of us freeing your people without bringing harm to anyone, we'll do it."

"It's not likely to happen that way," I said.

"I know," Father Josef said softly. He lay down, the pack under his head. "I know," he repeated.

                            *   *   *

We were not disturbed that day, and the following night we pushed farther north, sleeping again in the remains of a burned-out village fifty miles north of Luang Prabang.

Father Josef explained to us that Laos, Cambodia and Vietnam were filled with such places, the mute evidence of the terrible fighting that had gone on here for years.

The morning of the fifth night out found us a hundred miles north of the Laotian capital city, and the following night we pushed on toward the Vietnam border near the Laotian village of Muong Va.

During our push through the jungle we had to skirt several villages, and it became more and more apparent that Father Josef had not only an intimate knowledge of this country, but his information was current.

Although we had been lucky so far, and had not run into any patrols, Father Lars became increasingly nervous as we approached Vietnam.

Father Josef and I both expected the priest would soon demand that we turn around and go back. But it never came, and around four A.M. of our sixth day out, we came to the clearing across which was the border to Vietnam.

A good distance to the south was a Vietnamese border patrol hut. As we hid in the jungle at the edge of the clearing, Father Josef explained what we would have to do.

"The patrol is fairly lax here," he said. "But they do run spot checks, so we're going to have to be absolutely quiet."

"How about the Laotian forces?" I asked.

"There's a highway about five miles south of here that runs from Muong Va across the border to Lai Chau in Vietnam. There's a Laotian border patrol stationed there. But they're too disorganized to run full border surveillance."

I took the field glasses from him and studied the Vietnamese border patrol post. There was a dim light shining from the hut, but at this distance I could not pick out any activity.

From where we stood in the jungle, it was at least a quarter of a mile across the clearing to the protection of the jungle across the border.

"We'll crawl across," Father Josef said as I lowered the glasses. "Single file. Me in the lead. And not a sound."

Father Lars and I both nodded.

Father Josef looked once again toward the border post, then nodded. "By daybreak I want to be well away from the border. So let's get on with it."

He shifted his pack to a more comfortable position, then got down on his hands and knees and crawled out to the knee-high grass in the clearing.

Father Lars went next, and I brought up the rear, the ground soft and wet.

I could not see Father Josef in the lead because of the darkness, just Father Lars' backside about ten yards ahead of me.

About five minutes out, I stopped a moment to adjust the straps on my pack; they were cutting into my shoulders. When I looked up, it seemed that Father Lars had begun to swing too far to the right.

I was just about to start toward him, when a tremendous explosion lit up the night sky, the concussion lifting me off the ground and flinging me backwards.

My ears were ringing and spots danced in front of my eyes. Then I noticed blood running down from my nose as I picked myself up.

Lights were flashing over by the Vietnamese border post, and I thought I could hear sirens.

Father Josef suddenly appeared out of the grass, his nose also bleeding. He frantically motioned me back toward the jungle on the Laotian side.

"What about Father Lars?" I said, although I could not hear my own voice.

Father Josef shook his head. "Dead," the word formed on his lips.

We scrambled back to the jungle, and once we were within the relative safety of the trees, we got to our feet.

I could definitely hear the sirens across the clearing now, as my hearing came back.

"What the hell happened?" Father Josef snapped.

"I don't know," I said. "I stopped to fix my pack. When I looked up, it seemed like he had moved off to the right."

"Goddamn it. Goddamn it to hell," Father Josef swore. "It was a land mine. He didn't have a chance. The dirty bastards."

"I'm sorry—" I started, but he cut me off.

"We can't stay here. We'll have to go north."

"We're not going back?" I asked.

"Hell no!" Father Josef snapped. "We came to rescue your POWs. We're not stopping now."

"North?"

He nodded. "China. They'll never expect us to come that way."

"Can we cross their border?"

"It'll be difficult, but I've done it before," Father Josef said. But then he looked a little closer at me. "That is if you want to continue."

I glanced back at the field. A small grass fire had started when the mine had gone off. "Let's go," I said.

FIVE

We managed to make between five and ten miles that morning before dawn broke. But this morning there wasn't the luxury of a burned-out village to hide in, nor were the trees here large enough to crawl up into and rest.

The underbrush was thick, however, and Father Josef and I crawled into the worst of it, wrapped ourselves in sheets of dark green plastic to keep the dampness of the earth away from us, and spent a miserable day trying to rest.

I knew that Father Josef was thinking about Father Lars. So was I. And it would be difficult for me to face the abbot, Father Martin, and explain to him why Father Lars had died.

This assignment was different from the ones to which I've normally been assigned. I've been used to facing and dealing with a man or men out in the open. But this time I was sneaking around a jungle doing nothing more than following a priest, and avoiding all contact with anyone.

The countryside we had been traveling through had been steadily rising up from the jungle floor, and the next evening found us in the rugged mountain country which Father Josef said was a part of the Annamese Cordillera, which was the old name for the Vietnamese mountain chain.

The weather became sharply cooler as we continued to climb, and early the next morning, as the sun was coming up, we could see snow on the distant peaks.

We had stopped at a rough stone hut with a badly sagging thatched roof. Father Josef pointed to a pass far below us to the northeast.

"China," he said softly.

China had been called the sleeping giant. But over the past ten years it had begun to awaken to the twentieth century.

"How closely do they patrol their borders up here?" I asked.

Father Josef shook his head. "Not at all on foot," he said. "They run occasional helicopters through the passes, but only during the daytime."

I stared out across the range. "Do you know this country well enough to cross the mountains at night?"

"Yes," he said softly.

"Yen Minh isn't in the mountains, is it?"

"No," he said turning back to me. "It's in the foothills. But it's a tough two hundred miles from here . . . a hundred of which are in the mountains. The last hundred is through the hills, but there will be border patrols there—many of them."

"What are our chances?"

Father Josef shrugged. "We'll never be able to come back this way with your people, if that's what you mean. And as far as penetrating Yen Minh without detection, it depends upon whether or not the Vietnamese become suspicious about Father Lars' death so close to their border." He shook his head again. "I just don't know. We'll have to try it and see."

Although our sleeping arrangements were much more comfortable this morning than they had been yesterday, I spent another miserable day trying, without much success, to sleep.

I kept thinking about Father Lars dying there in the clearing along the Vietnamese border; about the POWs in the camp at Yen Minh; and about Captain Bruce who had died coming out.

Perhaps the abbot, Father Martin, had been right when he wondered if diplomatic means wouldn't be the better course of action. Perhaps I was on a fool's mission. Perhaps I'd get them all killed.

I've seldom had second thoughts about an assignment in the middle of the assignment. But this time I just didn't know.

Just before I finally dropped off to sleep, I turned to glance over at Father Josef wrapped in his blanket. He couldn't predict our chances of success either.

"We'll have to try it and see," his words ran through my mind. ". . . try it and see."

That evening we crossed the border into China without incident and began working our way east through the mountains, the wind whipping down from the snowy peaks, ice cold and penetrating.

Around two in the morning we heard the sound of a high-flying jet, and we watched its lights move slowly overhead and disappear to the northeast.

We slept that day beneath an overhanging rock, and near the end of the next evening, the ninth since we had left Chiang Khan, we crossed the Red

River over a not too sturdy footbridge, and then began to come down out of the mountains.

The tenth evening saw us well down into the foothills about fifty miles west of Yen Minh, and then we began running into the Chinese border patrols.

We had been generally paralleling the Vietnamese border, but keeping at least five miles within China in order to avoid any contact with the patrols. But twice we watched from hiding places as pairs of uniformed Chinese passed us by.

"Why are they so far from the border?" I asked after our second encounter.

"I don't know," Father Josef said, concerned.

"Can they know we're here?"

He thought a moment. "I don't think so. They're either running some kind of exercises, which they do from time to time, or else they're expecting trouble from the Vietnamese."

I looked at my watch. The luminous hands read a few minutes after two. "If this kind of activity extends all along the border, it's going to be too dangerous for us to stay here during the day."

"I was just thinking the same thing," Father Josef said. "We're going to have to cross the border before daybreak."

"Will we make it to Yen Minh tomorrow night?"

"With luck we will," Father Josef said. "But it'll be too late for us to make our move then. We'll have to find somewhere to hole up near the camp."

"Two more nights then," I said.

"We've come this far, we'll make it the rest of the way."

I nodded, less concerned now that we were this

close to Yen Minh. I would worry about what we were going to do when we got there.

We waited another ten minutes watching for any other border patrols, before we headed almost directly south toward the Vietnamese border.

Within one mile of the border we had not come across any other patrols, but we did come to a small, rapidly moving river.

"This is the Po," Father Josef said. "It merges downstream with the Red River, which flows past Hanoi and eventually empties into the Gulf of Tonkin near Haiphong."

Haiphong. Hearing Father Josef mention the name of North Vietnam's major seaport city was startling at this moment. If all else failed in our efforts to bring the POWs out normally, we would have an appointment in Haiphong. An appointment that would literally blow the lid off American relations here in the Far East.

Someone whistled behind us, and we spun around and crouched low.

Father Josef motioned for me to be silent as we both strained to listen.

The whistle came again, about a hundred yards through the woods, and then someone shouted something.

"Border patrol," Father Josef mouthed the words.

I nodded.

Another voice came through the woods, much closer now, and to our left.

We were being hemmed in here, the border to the right, soldiers straight ahead and to our left, and the river at our backs.

Other voices came now, even closer than before. It sounded as if two patrols were merging here at the river.

Without further hesitation Father Josef turned and carefully eased himself into the water. I was right behind him, the current snatching at my legs, the water coming down from the snowy mountain peaks ice cold.

Keeping close to the overhanging brush along the bank, we pushed downriver, stopping every few yards to listen for sounds behind us.

But there was nothing, and within fifteen minutes we had come around a sharp bend in the river where we pulled up short.

A hundred yards downstream a wooden bridge with squat stone pilings spanned the river parallel to the border. Even from where we hid on the bank, we could see at least a half dozen armed soldiers in huts on either side of the span, and two of them were leaning on the wooden railing staring down at the water.

A Vietnamese flag flew from a pole over one of the huts, and the soldiers all wore Vietnamese uniforms.

As long as the two soldiers remained leaning over the rail looking down, we were unable to move from our position. Once around the curve, we would be easily spotted.

The water was waist deep, and my legs were completely numb by the time one of the soldiers straightened up, lit a cigarette and moved off toward one of the huts.

The second soldier straightened up and called something after him, but the first man just laughed and continued toward the hut.

"Go on," I said to myself. "Follow him, you bastard."

The second man called out something again, but still the other continued toward the hut, finally disappearing inside.

The man by the rail said something else, then went across the bridge to the hut.

"Now," Father Josef said, and he started downstream.

I was right behind him, trying to make as little noise as possible, but my feet and legs were devoid of feeling and several times I stumbled and nearly fell headlong into the water.

A few yards from the bridge, one of the men from the other huts shouted something across the bridge and then started across the span.

With a burst of speed, Father Josef and I pushed the rest of the way to the bridge and then beneath it where we huddled next to one of the stone columns.

We could hear the soldier above us coming across the wooden planking of the bridge, but then suddenly he stopped.

Either he had seen us or had heard a noise.

The deck of the bridge was about fifteen feet overhead, and for several long seconds it was quiet. But then a stream of water came over the edge of the bridge, splashing noisily a few feet from where we stood in the waist-deep water. I almost laughed out loud. Father Josef was grinning.

The guard had come out of his hut to urinate over the railing. He hadn't heard or seen a thing.

At length he was finished. He belched and then we could hear him going back across the bridge to his hut. Seconds later it was quiet again.

Silently we moved around the stone piling, continued a few more feet downstream so that we could look up and see the railing on the other side, and then stopped, holding our breath as we listened for any sounds. But there was nothing.

Slowly, and keeping well toward the overhanging brush at the riverbank, we moved away from the protection of the bridge, not daring to look back until we were at least a hundred yards downstream.

When we finally stopped and looked up toward the bridge, nothing had changed, everything was quiet. We had made it. We were in Vietnam, less than fifty miles now from Yen Minh.

We made another ten miles directly away from the border that night, sleeping in a very damp cave on the riverbank that day.

The following evening, our eleventh since leaving Chiang Khan, we again paralleled the border, pushing hard and further down into low hill country that gradually gave way to the dense, semi-tropical forest of the lowlands.

Here, near the border of China, the countryside was wild and very sparsely populated. Although there would be no relatively comfortable abandoned villages in which we could hide out during the daylight hours, that disadvantage was far outweighed by the fact it was not likely that we would stumble into anyone.

We were far enough away from the border itself so that there was little likelihood that we would run into a patrol. Most of the evening we hiked easily, taking little pains to mask our passage.

Around two-thirty, we came upon the small town of Yen Minh itself, and by three-thirty we had skirted it to the south, and then had hiked northeast in search of the internment camp itself.

At this point, Father Josef's knowledge was very scanty. He had heard there was an internment camp somewhere to the northeast of Yen Minh, but nothing more.

For awhile I had visions of wandering around the North Vietnam countryside for days and days in search of the camp.

Around five in the morning, about a half an hour before we would have to stop, we came over the crest of a small hill. Beneath us, about a mile away, were the lights of a fairly small compound.

I had spotted it first, and I stopped. Father Josef followed suit.

"The camp?" I said softly.

"I can't imagine what else it would be," he said.

The entire camp was only a couple of hundred yards on a side, surrounded by a tall, ragged bamboo fence with tall guard towers at two diagonal corners.

Lights shown down on the interior of the compound from the towers and around the perimeter from lights strung up on the fence.

A paved road led away from the compound's main gate due south, from the village of Yen Minh and directly toward Hanoi I supposed.

We were crouching now on the hilltop too far away from the camp to see any activity below, although I suspected the POWs would be bedded down for the night. It was likely that the guards would not be overly alert either. Although Captain

Bruce had managed to escape, it had happened several weeks ago.

In any event, I did not think the guards would be looking outward for an attack. If anything, they would be watching the prisoners' barracks.

We continued to watch the camp for another twenty minutes until the eastern horizon began to lighten, and then we hiked back another half a mile, finally crawling into some deep underbrush.

We had replenished our water supply from the river, but we were running low on food. That didn't really matter now, I thought. By tomorrow night we would either be in control of the camp which had supplies, or we would be dead.

Father Josef was opening one of the last cans of C rations as I pulled out my Luger from beneath my robes and a small gun cleaning kit from my pack.

He watched me as I disassembled the automatic, carefully cleaning and oiling each piece. When I had it back together and loaded, he sighed deeply.

"You must understand that I will not participate in any killing," he said softly.

I looked up at him and nodded. "I understand, Father, and I respect that. But you must also understand what will probably have to be done down there."

He nodded. "They're just young boys, like soldiers in any other military service."

"Sworn to give their lives in defense of their country. But our only chance of getting out of here alive, is taking over the camp before the alarm can be sounded."

Father Josef reached over and touched my arm.

"I want you to at least think about another way of doing it," he said. "We have the rest of today. I don't think we should attempt our move until after midnight. Until after the camp is completely settled down for the night."

I looked at him for a long time. I was tired: bone weary from the overland trip, and mentally fatigued from thinking about exactly what he had just suggested.

But in ten days I had been unable to come up with any viable alternative. Even if I could hold the POWs back once they were released, taking prisoners would be just too risky.

The North Vietnamese had clearly made their choice in this matter when they refused to acknowledge the end of the war and give up the POWs after the hostilities had ceased.

Some of those men down there, like Captain Bruce, had been prisoners for ten years. Others had probably been here longer.

I reholstered my Luger, then lay down pulling the green plastic a little closer around me. The Vietnamese had had the upper hand for the past ten years. It was time now, no matter what it took, to bring our people home.

I dreamed that Father Josef was running down the hill toward the POW camp shouting that he didn't want to die. I was a couple of hundred yards behind him, but no matter how hard I tried, I could not seem to catch up.

As the priest neared the compound's walls, I could see thousands of Vietnamese soldiers all raising their automatic weapons to their shoulders.

I tried to shout for him to turn back, but I couldn't even do that, and silently the soldiers fired their weapons, cutting the priest to ribbons.

It was dark when I woke in a cold sweat. For a couple of seconds I lay there trying to get my bearings, but then I turned my head. Father Josef was already awake, and he was peering through the dense undergrowth toward the north.

"What is it?" I asked sitting up.

He glanced over at me. "Three trucks over the hill came in just after sunset."

"Into the camp?" I asked.

He shrugged. "It's the only road. I would presume so."

Three trucks would not be enough to transport one hundred and fifty POWs out of here, so they were probably bringing supplies. At least I hoped that's all it was. I hoped that somehow the Vietnamese hadn't gotten wind of the fact that we were here and had sent out for reinforcements.

It was a few minutes after ten P.M. Incredibly I had slept through the entire day. My muscles ached from lying on the hard ground, but I felt refreshed. Evidently I had needed the sleep.

"Do you want something to eat?" Father Josef asked.

"No. But I'd give almost anything to have a cigarette."

He smiled. "Maybe in a few hours."

I pulled my robe off over my head, then dressed in a pair of U.S. Army fatigue trousers, shirt and boots. I had carried them across Thailand, Laos and then China for this moment. Father Josef was watching me.

"The charade ends now," I said.

"If you're spotted you'll be shot on the spot, no questions asked."

"Shot as an American. Not as a priest from your order." I wrapped up my plastic bedroll and stuffed it along with my other gear back into my pack and secured the straps. "You can remain here, Father, or you can come along."

"What's your plan?" he asked as he finished packing his equipment.

"I'm going to sneak into the camp, probably through the north wall opposite the main gate, contact Colonel Powell, the senior POW, and then take the camp shortly before sunrise."

Father Josef seemed to think about that for a long moment. "Fine," he said. "I'll stay on the hill. But you'll need a diversion."

"Diversion?"

He nodded. "A couple of minutes before you hit, I'll wander down to the road and approach the main gate."

"It's too dangerous . . ." I started, but he cut me off.

"I know what I'm talking about. They won't start shooting if they see a lone priest coming down the road on foot. But they'll be damned curious. It'll draw the attention of the guards on the towers."

I wanted to protest, but I knew he was right. If this was going to be successful, we would need every advantage we could get.

I nodded, then held my watch up. "It's ten-twenty-seven on the dot."

Father Josef had looked at his watch, and he nodded. "You'll hit at five o'clock?"

"At five," I said. "It'll give me enough time to contact Powell and make sure his people are ready."

We looked at each other.

"Good luck, Father," I said. "And thanks for your help."

Father Josef smiled. "God bless you son."

SIX

Father Josef would remain hidden in the underbrush until shortly after four A.M. At that point he
would come down to the road and approach the
main gate. At a minute or two before five he would
present himself there, giving me and the POWs a
diversion.

Now it was a few minutes before midnight as I
lay on the crest of the hill looking down at the compound.

Three trucks were parked inside near one of the
low buildings, but I could see no activity down
there. Once again the camp was bedded down for
the night, although I was certain there were guards
on the towers.

I crawled back behind the hill, and keeping it
between me and the camp, hiked almost straight
east to where I knew the paved road would be.

The night was warm and oppressively humid,
but the sky was overcast, and the jungle very dark,
for which I was grateful.

Every twenty yards or so, I stopped in my tracks
and listened. But each time the only sounds I heard
were the ever-present night insects.

In fifteen minutes I had reached the road, and

for a minute or two I remained hidden in the jungle watching and listening. But the highway was deserted, nothing visible in either direction.

Silently I stepped out of the jungle and, keeping low, dashed across the road to the other side.

No alarm was sounded, no shots were fired, and once again I worked my way through the dense forest, finally turning north when I felt I had come far enough east to clear the camp.

I was worried about Father Josef. I did not want him to end up like Father Lars, and yet his plan for a diversion was a good one. Unlike him, however, I wasn't a hundred percent convinced that the guards on the towers wouldn't open fire as soon as he was spotted.

About a quarter of a mile off the road, the land dipped down into a marshy area, and I found myself slogging through knee-deep water, making it almost impossible to move without making noise. But the marsh was narrow and within a few minutes I was once again on dry land hurrying north.

Gradually I began angling west back toward the camp, and by twenty after twelve I came to the clearing that had been cut all around the compound. I was well north of the camp, just above the rear wall, almost directly across from the main gate.

From where I hid behind the trees, I studied the camp and its approaches. Nothing had changed. There was still no activity below, although now I could clearly make out the head of at least one guard on the northwest tower.

I would be exposed to his view for about a hundred yards between where I was and the safety of the compound walls. Once I got close enough, the tower guards would not be able to see me.

It was getting late, and there was a lot to be accomplished before Father Josef came down the road; so without further hesitation, I got down on my stomach, crawled out from the protection of the dark jungle, and started down the clearing toward the bamboo perimeter wall.

As I got closer to the camp, I could hear the low hum of running machinery. The electrical generators, I supposed. But there were no other sounds.

Halfway across I stopped and chanced a look up toward the guard tower. The soldier up there had his back to me, and as I watched, a match flared, and he lit himself a cigarette.

Quickly then, so I could take advantage of his temporary loss of night vision, I crawled the rest of the way to the bamboo wall where I scrambled up to a crouch in the deep shadows.

Still no alarm had been sounded. The only noises in the night were the insects and the generator inside.

After I caught my breath I looked a little closer at the bamboo wall. It was solid, the individual trunks lashed together with wire.

I pulled out my stiletto and was about to probe the bamboo to see if it would be possible to cut through it, but at the last moment I stopped.

There was something about the wire lashings that seemed odd.

I looked closer at the wire. It was insulated. But why?

Careful now not to brush up against it, I traced the wire down the wall, finally coming to a spot where a dozen of the wire strands all came together, then disappeared through the wall.

The wire carried an electrical current; there was little doubt of it now in my mind. But it wasn't a current meant to kill. These were alarm wires. The entire perimeter fence was wired with alarms. There was no way I was going to get through it.

I looked up. The only other way was over the wall. Impossible with the guards in their towers.

But we had come too far for me to give it up now. The North Vietnamese had held the upper hand for too long. It was our turn now. The one hundred and fifty POWs inside were going to be free by morning.

Quickly but silently I worked my way along the wall to the northwest corner just at the base of the guard tower. Once there I pulled off my pack.

The jagged top of the compound's wall was about fifteen feet overhead. The floor of the guard tower was about ten feet above that..

With my stiletto I cut the straps off my pack and lengthened them on their slides as far as they would go. Then I tied them together, making a strap around ten feet long with one of the large buckles at one end.

It was barely long enough, but I had nothing else.

Stepping back a foot or two away from the wall, I looked up. The only way the guard would be able to see me down here, was if he leaned over the edge —which he would most certainly do if he heard a noise.

There was no other way, I told myself again, tensing.

As gently as I could, I tossed the strap up to the top of the wall, buckle first, the end of it just barely clearing the jagged ends and making a soft click.

I had to jump up to catch my end of the strap and pull it down toward me.

As I hoped would happen, the wide buckle became wedged between the bamboo logs.

I waited there, one hand tugging on the strap for a minute or two, staring up at the guard tower. But nothing happened. The soldier up there had not heard a thing.

If I could get to the top of the wall without triggering the alarm wires; if I could climb up the guard tower without being heard by the soldier above, or seen by the soldier in the tower on the other side of the camp; if I could take out this soldier—all this without being seen or heard by anyone else—I would be over the first hurdle and we'd have a chance.

I had to smile at myself. I'm used to taking risks, but this was pushing my luck and abilities to the limit.

There was no other way, though, I told myself.

I took off my boots and socks and laid them down by my pack. Then, making sure that the strap dangling from the top of the wall was secure, started up, making sure I kept my feet away from the wires.

The surface of the bamboo was fairly rough, and the climb was easy so that in a few seconds I was at the top hanging onto one of the rear legs of the tower, my head just clearing the wall.

Although it was well lit up, the compound was quiet, and for several long seconds, I clung there watching the guard tower on the other side. The spotlight there was on, and I could see a machine gun on its mounts, but no soldier.

It was possible that he was sitting down out of sight, but I wanted to make sure before I climbed up and exposed myself to view.

Then I noticed a movement at the base of the far tower, and I froze.

Someone was there. In the shadows. For a fleeting moment I wondered if one of the POWs hadn't gotten out of the barracks and was making an escape attempt. If that was the case, and he was caught, we would be finished here before we had even begun.

The person stepped out into the light, and I could see it was a Vietnamese soldier. Probably the guard from the tower. But what the hell was he doing?

He went straight across the compound to a long narrow building near the main gate. Before he went inside he turned and waved toward the tower I was perched beneath; then starting to unbuckle his equipment belt, he stepped inside.

The building had to be a latrine. He was going in to relieve himself.

No one else appeared to be in the far tower, which meant it was likely that each tower was manned by only one soldier.

My luck was running high.

I pulled myself the rest of the way up and over the wall, and then with my stiletto clenched in my teeth, climbed up the last ten feet to the base of the tower.

Crouching there on the ledge just below the side skirt, finally hidden from view by anyone within the compound, I took my stiletto out of my mouth, tensed my muscles, and started to rise.

At that moment the guard appeared directly

above me, our eyes meeting.

He started to open his mouth as he brought his rifle around, but at that moment I pushed up, burying the stiletto in his throat, slicing his carotid artery, blood spurting everywhere as he stumbled backwards.

I was over the edge and inside the tower on top of him in a second as he sank down to the floor, his eyes glazing over, and the spurting blood slowing and then stopping.

Yanking the stiletto out of his neck and wiping it on his shirt front, I looked over the edge of the tower skirt down toward the latrine.

The other guard was still inside. But he would not be there too long.

Quickly I went through the opening in the tower floor and scrambled down the ladder into the compound where I crouched a moment at the side of a building.

The compound was still quiet. No alarm had been sounded, and the other guard was still in the latrine.

Keeping low, I hurried to the front of the building, then dashed across the compound to the latrine near the main gate.

If there was anyone awake, anyone looking out one of the windows, exposed here like this, I would be a dead man. But still no alarm was sounded.

I eased along the length of the building to the doorway. Then, flattening myself against the wall, I peered around the edge inside.

The other guard, his trousers down around his ankles, was hunched over a bamboo rail relieving himself into an open pit. He was looking down at his shoes, and only in the last second as I leaped into the building did he look up, but by then it was too late for him.

In two steps I was on him, my left hand clamping over his mouth as it opened for a shout, and my right hand driving the stiletto into his chest just below his left breast.

His body stiffened, shuddered once, and then relaxed, folding up and slipping over the edge of the bamboo rail, down into the latrine pit.

I spun on my heel and went back to the doorway where I looked outside, half expecting to see soldiers pouring out of the barracks.

But there was nothing. The camp seemed peaceful. Sleeping. Nothing had changed.

When I turned back, I noticed that the guard's rifle was leaning up against the wall. I snatched it up. It was a Kalashnikov, the Soviet assault rifle used by half the armies and terrorist groups in the world. But its presence here came as a complete surprise to me.

We had always thought the Chinese were the exclusive arms suppliers to the North Vietnamese. But a Soviet weapon here? That in itself was a hell of a piece of intelligence that I would have to make sure got back.

Back at the doorway again I looked outside. To my left was the main gate. Directly across was a large building which I took to be the administration center, and probably the guards' dining hall. Behind it were two buildings, one of them probably the guards' barracks, and the other a windowless structure that was probably either the armory or some kind of a supply building.

To the right were a half dozen long, very low, crudely constructed huts with thatched roofs, the corrugated iron sides devoid of windows or openings.

No doubt they were the barracks where our POWs were being kept, had been kept, some of them for more than ten years. It made my blood boil just looking at the huts.

I stepped out of the building, hesitated a moment, and then raced across the compound to the first of the huts where I stopped at the corrugated metal door.

A two-by-four bar secured the door, and laying the rifle down, I carefully eased the bar out of its slots, trying to make as little noise as possible, and set it aside.

Picking up the rifle, I eased the door open and looked inside.

A terrible, hot stench blasted out of the building causing my stomach to flop over.

If our POWs had been subjected to these kinds of conditions for ten years or more, it would be a wonder if any of them could move, let alone help me take over this camp, and then make their way all the way back to Thailand.

I could see Captain Bruce's emaciated, toothless figure beneath the sheets back at the hospital in Bethesda. Whatever feelings of remorse I had had about killing the two tower guards completely left me.

Slipping inside the fetid hut, I closed the door behind me, then pulled out my penlight and switched it on.

The sight that greeted me shook me so badly that I nearly dropped the rifle and the light.

At least three dozen men and a couple of women, all of them half nude and filthy dirty, lay awake on bundles of stinking grass looking up at me. Their eyes were wide, their skulls were shaved, and their ribs were outlined sharply above their protruding stomachs.

"My God," I said softly, my stomach heaving. "Oh my God."

Someone on the floor right next to me mumbled something, and fingers gripped my bare ankles.

"Colonel Powell," I said softly. "Is Colonel Powell here?"

"English," the emaciated figure at my feet croaked.

"He's speaking English," someone else deeper in the building said.

"Colonel Powell?"

"Here," a man said. There was a shuffling sound near the back of the hut, and I shined my tiny light that way.

An unbelievably thin, cadaverous figure came into the circle of light and stopped a few feet away from me.

"Colonel Powell, Gary S., United States Air Force, sir," he said. "Captain Bruce got out okay?"

"Yes he did, Colonel," I said, softly. "I've come to take you and your people home."

"Home," Colonel Powell barely breathed the word. His eyes filled with tears. "My God . . . home. Choppers? Did you bring choppers?"

"No. No choppers. We've got a long way to go, Colonel. But by morning you will all be free men and women."

They were all up now, mouthing words, some of them crying. I was afraid they'd make too much noise and wake up the other guards.

"You all have to be quiet now," I said, raising my voice as much as I dared.

An instantaneous silence descended on the hut. Powell stood at attention. I suddenly had a premonition that this was not going to go very well. They were too damned weak, too psychologically ruined by their captivity to be of much help.

"Listen to me, Colonel," I said. "I managed to get in and kill the two tower guards. But that's it. I'm going to need your help to take over this camp."

The tears were streaming down Powell's cheeks.

"But we can't make any noise, and we have to take over the camp before they're able to establish communications with Hanoi."

Powell just looked at me.

"Do you understand what I'm saying, Colonel?"

He stepped toward me, reached out a boney hand and touched my chest, a wonderment coming into his eyes.

"You're real. Jesus H. Christ, you're real!"

"I'm real, Colonel," I said, my heart going out to him, and to the other pitiful figures staring up at me. "But I'm going to need your help to get you and your people out of here. Do you understand what I'm saying to you?"

He was nodding his head, his entire gaunt figure shaking. "Oh Christ. Fucking A, I understand you." He looked around at the others who were getting to their feet. Then he looked back. "Who the hell are you?"

"Nick Carter," I said. "I came in with a Belgian priest from Thailand. He's outside the camp now. We're going to get you the hell out of here. But first we have to take over the camp and neutralize their communications facility."

"Colonel Thai Nong," Powell hissed. The others were crowding forward now, the stench overpowering. "You say you've taken out the tower guards?"

"Yes. But how many other troops are here?"

"A bunch," Colonel Powell said, and suddenly he seemed a little taller, a little fuller, much stronger than before. "What have you got planned? A Belgian priest, you say?"

I nodded. "How many POWs are here?"

"One hundred and forty-four as of last night's roll call," Powell said. "Among them are six women."

"All right," I said. "First of all we have to take over the camp. But without any alarms being raised. Who runs the communications facility?"

"Colonel Thai Nong," Powell said.

"Then we have to keep him alive," I said.

They all looked at me.

"First of all, we eliminate the troops. We take over the camp, saving Colonel Thai Nong to do our communications for us."

The strength seemed to be flowing into Powell and his people.

"Then, once we normalize the camp—"

Powell interrupted me. "You do have a plan for getting us out of here?"

I nodded.

"That's good enough for me. We'll take the camp, and go from there," he said. "What about Bob? Is he okay?"

I debated for a moment lying to them, but I

could not. "He made it to a fishing village near Haiphong, then took an open fishing boat to Luzon in a storm where he was picked up. We got him back to Bethesda, but he died."

Colonel Powell took a deep breath and then let it out slowly. "Do they know about us?"

I didn't know what he meant. I shook my head.

"The American public. Do they know we're here?"

"Shit," I said. "No. They think you're all probably dead."

Powell and a couple of the others laughed. "They're in for a surprise."

"The entire world is," I said, but Powell had turned to his people.

"Alec, you and Jones and Norbert, get the weapons. Stan and Anderson, get the other barracks. Let them know what's happening. I want all my officers back here within ten minutes."

"Yes, sir," several men snapped, and there was a flurry of activity. Two of the men slipped out of the barracks through a hole in the floor beneath one of the straw beds.

"What's the situation out there?" Powell asked me.

"I came over the wall, up the northwest tower," I said. "The guard there is dead. The other tower guard was in the latrine. I got him there."

Powell nodded, then looked at the Kalashnikov. "Was that a surprise?"

I nodded. "I thought the Chinese were supplying weapons here."

"They were, but the Russians had their hand in it as well," Powell said smiling. He shook his head.

"Sweet Jesus, Carter, have we got a lot to say when we get back."

"We have a long way to go, Colonel. Let's take it a step at a time."

"Fine by me," he said. "We'll brief my officers, and then you and I will go for Thai Nong while the others take care of the grunts."

I offered the Kalashnikov to him, but he declined it. "Put it aside for now," he said. "We're going to have to do this without noise."

My eyes narrowed.

"Evidently you're not aware of the situation at Yen Minh?"

I shook my head.

"Yeah. Well our intelligence twelve years ago wasn't any better."

"What's at Yen Minh?"

Colonel Powell smiled grimly. "A strategic missile installation, along with five thousand government troops."

"Jesus," I breathed the single word. No wonder the Chinese had so many border patrols. And we had come within a couple of miles of the place.

SEVEN

Whatever doubts I had had about these men being capable of action were completely dispelled in the first ten minutes or so. I should have known better. Captain Bruce had been in the same condition, and yet he had managed his incredible journey.

As Colonel Powell's officers from the other barracks began slipping up through the hole in the floor, an amazing collection of weapons began appearing. Bits and pieces of glass, shards of metal, the edges razor sharp, a half dozen knives, two pistols, a couple of hand grenades, a land mine, and two rifles in addition to the Kalashnikov I had brought.

Two sets of Vietnamese uniforms appeared, and two of Powell's men slipped into them.

"Where are the tower guards?" Powell asked.

"One is in the latrine, the other is up in the northwest tower."

"You're certain they're both dead?"

"They're dead," I said.

Powell turned to the men in the uniforms. "I want you two up in the towers. Make yourself conspicuous, but quiet." He glanced at his other people. "We're going to be free in a very short time.

We're going to remain so . . . dead or alive. Agreed?"

Everyone nodded.

"Silence is the operative word then," Powell said, looking pointedly at his two tower guards. "But if something goes wrong, I want this entire camp sprayed."

They both nodded. One of them took the Kalashnikov from me. They checked the compound from a small hole near the door and then slipped outside.

Another of Powell's people took up position at the small peephole, and a couple of minutes later he turned back and gave us the thumbs-up sign. The tower guards were in place.

"Now tell me about this priest," Powell said. "Who is he and where is he?"

"He's Father Josef. Runs a leper hospital just across the Laotian border in Thailand. He got me here, and he's going to get us back." I looked at my watch. It was nearly one. "He'll approach the main gate at five . . . or at least that was the plan. I was looking for a diversion."

"We'll be done by then," Powell said. He glanced down at my feet. "You didn't come all that way barefoot?"

"No," I said, and I told him how I had entered.

"I want his equipment picked up as soon as we've secured the camp," Powell said to one of his officers. "And I want someone up on the towers to let Al and David know that the priest will be showing up at five."

"How about the women?" I asked. He had said there were six among the POWs. There were only two in this building.

Powell looked sharply at me. "They fight with us," he said.

"Where are the other four?"

Again an odd expression crossed Powell's features. "Two here, two in the blue hut, and . . ." he hesitated.

One of the women stepped forward. "Sister Therese and Sister Mary," she said softly. "Catholic nuns. They're with Colonel Thai Nong. They're his . . . servants."

"I see," I said.

"Any other questions?" Powell asked. I shook my head. "Blue and green barracks, you'll take the guards' quarters. No noise. You'll have to coordinate your strike front to back so you'll have the entire barracks covered without any lags."

Several men nodded, and Powell turned to another group.

"Yellow barracks takes the supply building, number one priority weapons and ammunition, of course." Powell looked around at the others, apparently searching for a specific face in the dim circle of light from my penlight. "Is Phil here?"

"Right here, Colonel," a bald, toothless man said, stepping into the light.

"What about communications? What can we do before all hell breaks loose to make absolutely certain that Thai Nong does not get off a message, and yet still not screw up the communications facility."

"The radio will be easy," the man said. "I'll just ground out the antenna. The phone line might be a bit more difficult. If we cut it, the trouble will show up. I'll have to do a little rewiring on the terminal."

"How long will it take you?"

"Fifteen minutes."

Powell thought a moment.

They were a hell of a lot better organized here than I thought they would be. Yet I could not stop worrying about the garrison just a few miles down the road at Yen Minh. Within minutes of an alert, we could have several thousand Vietnamese troops breathing down our necks.

"All right, listen up. This is going to be tight, but it should work," Powell said.

Everyone seemed to lean forward.

"Phil will go out immediately to take care of the communications. Meanwhile, the rest of you will return to your people and brief them. I want you all ready and standing by within ten minutes."

No one said a thing.

"My people from this barracks are going to take the perimeter, including the main gate and the alarm system. Meanwhile, our visitor here and I are going to pay a visit to Thai Nong."

"What about the timing?" one of his people asked.

"As soon as Phil comes back here, we strike. Keep your lookouts posted. The moment Carter and I step out the front door and head across the compound to administration, I want you on the move. If something happens over there, and Thai Nong pulls the switch, I don't want anyone in or near the barracks."

The man nodded, and Powell looked around at the others.

"Questions?"

There were none.

"Then we start now. Go!"

There was a flurry of activity as Powell's officers scrambled through the hole in the floor to return to their barracks, and his communications man slipped out the door, a few crude tools in hand, to deactivate the camp's communications facility.

I had turned my penlight off, and now that my eyes had adjusted to the darkness, I could see that a small amount of light came in from a narrow gap between the top of the walls and the roof.

Powell's people here in this barracks, including the two women, had taken their makeshift weapons out of hiding and were now ready to do whatever it took to free themselves.

They were counting on Father Josef and me to lead them out of here once they took over the camp. Only it wasn't going to be that easy. Some of these people would almost certainly die in the attempt. I just hoped that we could keep that number as low as possible.

It took Colonel Powell's communications man something under twenty minutes to do his work and return to the barracks. He was out of breath, the effort dragging him out. It would be totally impossible for this man, at least, to walk across Vietnam and then Laos. He'd never make it.

"All right people, listen up," Powell whispered. His people all pressed forward. "We strike now. And under no circumstances will there be any prisoners."

Powell had a razor sharp bayonet. He raised it. "Freedom."

"Freedom," the other POWs chorused.

Powell turned to me. "You ready, Carter?"

I nodded. "We take Thai Nong alive," I said softly.

Powell stiffened. "No way."

"Listen to me, Colonel. There's no doubt that Thai Nong maintains a regular communications schedule with Hanoi. We need him to tell us when and how the schedule works. We don't have choppers here to take you out of the country. Getting out is going to take some work, more time, and a lot of luck. Thai Nong is going to help give us the time we need."

Powell was torn. I could see it clearly on his face. On the one hand he knew that killing Thai Nong would give us nothing, militarily. And yet there was ten years or more of pent-up hatred inside of him.

He finally nodded, however. "We keep him alive only as long as we absolutely need him. But if anything goes wrong, anything at all, he will be the first one to die. Understood?"

"Understood," I said.

He looked around at the others. "Let's do it then," he said, and we moved immediately to the front door where the lookout stepped aside.

"All clear out there?" Powell asked.

The man nodded.

Powell opened the door and we all slipped outside one by one. Almost immediately POWs from the other barracks began coming out into the compound. It was strange to see this many people and hear absolutely nothing but the night insects and the generator producing the camp's electricity.

Powell and I split away from the main group and headed quickly across the compound to the administration building.

Reaching the side of the building, we held up a moment to let the others get in place. Powell was shaking. At first I thought it was from fatigue or fright, but by the look on his face I realized he was shaking with rage. This was going to be a bloodbath. And I could not blame them. Yet when Father Josef showed up later this morning I was going to have a hard time justifying what went on here.

As quickly as the compound had filled with POWs, it seemed to empty. I knew they were all out there, but they were hidden now in the deeper shadows behind the buildings.

The guards were visible in the towers, and from where we stood it was impossible to tell that they were imposters.

Powell touched me on the arm. I looked around, and he pointed toward the rear of the building.

As we headed back I pulled out my Luger, levered a round into the firing chamber and flicked the safety off.

A portable air conditioner jutted from one of the rear windows, and Powell pointed to it. Thai Nong's quarters. The man definitely enjoyed a certain luxury out here.

We hurried around the corner and along the back of the building to the other side, where Powell opened a window and looked inside.

A second later he motioned for me to boost him up. When he was in, I climbed up over the high windowsill into what turned out to be a large bathroom with a huge wooden tub.

Powell moved softly to the door, listened a moment, then slowly opened it, looked out, then slipped out into a corridor.

I was right behind him. Toward the front of the building the corridor opened up into what appeared to be the camp's office. Toward the rear of the building, across the corridor from where we stood, was a door which Powell motioned toward.

We glided across to it, and as Powell was about to put his ear to it and listen, the door started to come open.

We both leaped to the side, flattening ourselves against the wall as a young woman, nude, came out of the room, closing the door behind her.

As she started to turn to come down the corridor, she spotted us. Her eyes went wide and her mouth opened.

I stepped past Powell and clamped my right hand over her mouth just as she was about to scream.

"We're friends," I whispered urgently.

The woman struggled for just a moment, but then her body went limp.

"Sister Therese," Powell said. "It's me. Colonel Powell."

The woman's eyes were still wide, but she nodded that she understood, and I took my hand away.

"Is Thai Nong in there?" I whispered.

She glanced fearfully toward the door, but then nodded.

"Is he sleeping?"

She nodded again, and then suddenly realizing that she was nude, covered her breasts with both hands, tears suddenly coming to her eyes.

"Go to your quarters. Get dressed and stay there. We've come to free you and the others," I said.

"Where is Sister Mary?" Powell asked.

She looked at him, tears coming even faster.

"Is she here?" Powell asked. "Is she all right?"

The woman shook her head. "Dead," she whispered.

Powell went rigid, then tried to shove past me to get at the door, but I knew what was coming, and I managed to hold him back.

"When did she die?" I asked.

"Two nights ago."

"Did Thai Nong kill her?"

She shook her head. "Sister Mary took her own life . . ." she started, but she could not continue.

"Go to your room now and get dressed. But no matter what happens, stay there until someone comes for you. Do you understand?"

She looked at me and then Powell, nodded her head, then padded past us down the corridor and into her room.

"We need Thai Nong, Colonel," I said. "We need him."

Powell said nothing, but his knuckles were white on the handle of his bayonet.

I listened at the door for a moment, but I could hear nothing other than the sound of the air conditioner. I took a deep breath, let it out slowly, then softly turned the handle on the door. I eased it open a crack and looked over my shoulder.

Powell's teeth were bared like an animal ready for attack.

Tensing my muscles and raising my Luger, I shoved the door all the way open and stepped into the room.

A slightly built man with dark hair was lying

nude on his back on a wide sleeping mat in the middle of the room.

His head jerked up when I came in. He blinked several times, then started to scramble to the right toward a low table which held several pieces of electronic equipment, including a short wave radio set.

"Stop or you die!" I snapped.

He was at the table and reaching for a switch on one of the pieces of equipment.

"The dynamite!" Powell shouted.

I was across the small room in a couple of steps, my weight shifting to my left foot. I kicked out with my right, catching Thai Nong high on the chest, sending him sprawling backwards.

Powell shoved me aside as Thai Nong regained his balance and dove for the table reaching out with his right hand for the switch.

Powell's razor-sharp bayonet flashed in the dim light coming from one of the pieces of equipment, hit the table with a dull crack, and Thai Nong fell back screaming, blood pumping from his wrist where the bayonet had completely severed his hand.

"Jesus!" I shouted. I shoved my Luger in my belt as I leaped toward Thai Nong. The man, still screaming in pain, swung the bloody stump at me. I sidestepped it and clipped him neatly on the jaw with a right hook, and he went down.

"Give me a piece of rope or cord," I shouted.

Outside I could hear the sounds of a struggle, but for the moment whatever else was going on didn't really matter. If Thai Nong died, our chances of escape would be next to nothing. We needed him.

Powell was just standing there, the bloody bayonet in his hand, a grim look of satisfaction in his eyes.

"Powell," I yelled.

He seemed to come around.

"We can't let him die!"

Powell pulled off the piece of thin rope holding his trousers up and handed it to me. As I was tying the cord around Thai Nong's forearm a few inches above the bloody stump at his wrist, Powell rummaged around the room. When I looked around, I saw that he had found a swagger stick which he tossed over.

I made a tourniquet, tightening it until the blood slowed, then stopped, and finally tied it in place with the ends of the cord.

Thai Nong was now in no immediate danger of bleeding to death, but he had lost too much blood for him to be of any use to us without medical attention.

"Are there any medics here?" I asked.

Powell nodded. "There's a camp doctor."

"One of theirs?"

Powell nodded.

"Get him before he's killed. We have to get this man on his feet or we'll all die. Do you understand what the hell I'm saying, Colonel?"

Powell nodded again, stared a moment longer at Thai Nong, then turned and hurried out of the room.

There was still a pulse at Thai Nong's neck, but it was weak. He needed medical attention and soon.

I stared at him for a long moment. I understood what it was to be a soldier, to fight and die for your country. And I understood what it meant to follow orders. But from what I had seen here so far, Thai Nong was no ordinary soldier simply following orders. He was a madman, a degenerate who had used his prisoners for his own perverse ends.

It would be so easy to just let him die.

"Is he dead?" a woman said from the doorway.

I spun around. Sister Therese, dressed now in black pajamas, was staring beyond me at Thai Nong's figure.

"No," I said. "But he's lost a lot of blood. Colonel Powell is going for the doctor."

She came all the way into the room and knelt down beside Thai Nong. She looked at me, then back down at him, and calmly and dispassionately she spit in his face.

"Sister . . ." I started to say, but she looked at me again, a calmness coming to her eyes.

"It's all right now," she said. Her voice held a slight French accent. "I am a nurse. I will help."

I wanted to say something to her. I wanted to find some words of comfort, but there was nothing that I could say that would erase what had happened to her over the past years, so I kept my silence.

The front door of the building clattered open ten minutes later. There was a commotion in the corridor, and Colonel Powell and two other POWs appeared in the doorway.

"Did you bring the doctor?" I asked looking up.

Powell came in. "I was too late. He was already dead."

"Damn," I swore.

"It is all right," Sister Therese said softly. "He

only needs a transfusion. There are medical records in the dispensary. I will be able to manage."

"You will help him?" I asked. "You'll save his life?"

"It is important?"

"Very," I said.

"Then I will manage," she said calmly. She looked up at the others. "Bring him to the dispensary. And be gentle lest he die."

Powell hesitated for just a moment, but then he motioned for the other two. "Do what Sister Therese says." He looked at them. "He *will* not die!"

"Yes, sir," they mumbled, coming the rest of the way in.

They picked him off the floor and left with Sister Therese.

"We have the camp?" I asked, getting to my feet.

Powell nodded. He seemed weak now.

"Casualties?"

He managed a smile. "Not one . . . on our side."

The communications man came into the room. "The telephones are back in service, and I took the ground off the radio antenna."

"Good," Powell said. "Disconnect the dynamite firing circuit and the alarm system."

"Yes, sir," he said.

"Do any of your people read Vietnamese?" I asked.

"All of us do," Powell said. "We've been here a long time."

"You'd better get your people to search for the communications and installation operations procedures, then. We're going to need them."

Powell nodded. "Take care of the comm logs,

Phil," he said. "I'll have someone else go through the orderly room files."

"Right," the communications man said from where he was studying the equipment on the table.

"All right, Carter. Now let's you and I get started on implementing your plan for getting us the hell out of here," Powell said.

"We have to wait for Father Josef. He will be here at five. That gives us a couple of hours for your people to get something decent to eat. I have a feeling you haven't had a substantial meal in a while."

"We're already working on it," Powell said. "But none of us really give a damn. We want to get the hell out of here. The sooner the better."

"The first thing we need is weapons and Vietnamese uniforms. You're all being conscripted into the Vietnamese Army."

Colonel Powell and I left Thai Nong's quarters and headed down the corridor toward the front door.

"There aren't enough uniforms for all of us," he said.

"Suit up as many as you can, then. The rest will have to be POWs who we're transferring. But I want everyone armed."

"They will be," Powell said.

We stepped outside, and suddenly something drew my eyes upwards toward the top of the perimeter fence. My stomach flopped over.

I have seen death and destruction. I have seen blood and gore. And I have killed men with my bare hands. But never in my career as an AXE killmaster have I seen a sight more gruesome than what I was looking at now.

Impaled on the jagged points at the top of the fence were human heads. Dozens of them. Evidently they were the heads of the Vietnamese soldiers who had been assigned as guards at this POW camp.

"My God," I said softly.

Powell was looking at me. "We'll all be debriefed when we get back," he said. "Including you. I'm telling you now, we'll all deny what you're seeing here. This never happened."

"It never should have happened, Colonel."

"It was more than ten years in the making. And no one who hasn't gone through what we've gone through could understand it. So . . . it never happened."

I nodded after a few seconds. "It never happened. But get them down from there, Colonel. Now!"

Powell just looked at me.

"What have they turned you into?"

He started to say something, but then a look of surprise crossed his face, and he glanced up at the heads. His shoulders suddenly sagged. "Oh, God," he said. "Oh, God."

EIGHT

There were only one or two bodies out in the compound, but inside the guards' barracks were bodies being hacked apart. Blood was spread everywhere.

When Colonel Powell and I stepped inside, we were stopped in our tracks of the enormity of what was happening.

Some of the POWs were sitting on the floor, in the middle of the gore, singing. Others were methodically hacking apart the bodies. Still others were painting slogans on the walls with blood.

One of the women had cut the penis off one of the guards, and she was holding it up, staring at it.

"What have we become?" Powell said softly.

I looked at him, but said nothing.

"Out!" he shouted. "Everyone out of here!"

Some of them looked up, dull vacant expressions in their eyes. Most of them ignored Powell.

"Out!" Powell screamed at the top of his lungs. He lunged forward, grabbed the bloody organ from the woman, yanked her to her feet, and slapped her hard across the face.

That brought everyone around. The singing stopped, and they all looked at Powell.

"I want you out in the assembly yard, in formation. Now!" he shouted.

Slowly then, almost hesitantly, the POWs shuffled out of the building.

"We've become animals," Powell said to me. "We've become something as bad and vile as Thai Nong."

I reached out and touched his shoulder. "Before we leave, we're going to clean this up and bury the bodies. Then we're going to forget what happened here."

Powell shook his head. "We will never forget this."

"No one else will ever know about it," I said. "I promise you."

Powell looked around at the shambles. He shook his head, then turned and we left the building.

POWs, some of them heavily armed now with weapons from the armory, were gathering on the assembly field in front of the administration building. No one was talking, and they all walked with heads bowed, averting their eyes from the heads stuck atop the bamboo fence.

"Squad leaders, get your people in formation. This is a military unit," Powell shouted.

He and I stood at the head of the formation that was slowly beginning to take shape.

"Give me a head count," Powell shouted.

Slowly, one by one the squad leaders reported. Everyone was present or accounted for. Sister Therese and two other POWs were still at the dispensary with Thai Nong. The communications man was still working on the equipment in administration, and we now knew that Sister Mary, the other nun whom Thai Nong had used, was dead.

Including Powell, there were one hundred and forty-three POWs, most of them on the verge of collapse, all standing there roughly at attention.

Powell turned to me and saluted. "All prisoners present or accounted for, sir."

I returned his salute, then turned to the assembly. "At ease," I said. "And as of this moment you will no longer consider yourselves prisoners of war. You are a fighting unit." I waited a moment for that to sink in. A few of them straightened up, but most of them just stared down at their feet.

"We've taken this camp, but if we're going to get out of Vietnam in one piece, we're going to have to begin working together, starting now. Is that clear."

There was silence.

"Is that clear?" I shouted.

"Yes, sir," a number of them mumbled.

"I can't hear you!" I shouted.

"Yes, sir," most of them shouted.

"That's better," I said. "But I'm going to tell you right now that unless we do pull together, you might as well give up. We can call Hanoi and tell them to send up replacements. Each of you can go back to your life as a POW, back to your stinking hovels."

"Carter, I don't think . . ." Powell started to say, but I cut him off.

"Bullshit!" I roared. "For ten years or more you have been prisoners. Damn few people know of your existence. Your families think you're dead. Well maybe you are."

"No," several men shouted. They were getting

mad. It was exactly what I wanted.

"Then lets act like soldiers. Let's act like a military unit."

The rows and columns began to straighten up. But still no one would look up at the heads on the perimeter fence.

"We're going to spend the day here getting ready. At 0500, that's just a couple of hours from now, a priest will be showing up. He is Father Josef from a medical facility in Thailand. He brought me this far, and he's going to help bring us back. Before he gets here this camp will be cleaned up, and every body buried."

No one said a thing. I turned to Powell.

"Get your officers started on that," I said. "Then I want your people fed, clothed and armed. Guards should be posted on the fence, and any of your people needing medical attention should get it immediately. I expect we will be leaving here in the early evening. I want everyone as well fed and rested as possible."

"It'll be done," Powell said.

"All right. As soon as you get your people started on that, come over to the dispensary. We're going to have to see what we can get out of Thai Nong."

Powell nodded, and I turned on my heel and strode across the compound to the dispensary next to the administration building.

The medical facility was contained in two rooms, one of them an examining room and laboratory, the other equipped with a half dozen low cots.

Thai Nong was lying on one of the cots, and lying next to him on another cot was one of the

POWs, his left arm out, a thin plastic tube connecting him to the camp commander.

Sister Therese was listening to Thai Nong's chest with a stethescope. When I came in she looked up.

"How is he doing?" I asked.

"He will live," the nun said. "I gave him one unit of plasma, and he's receiving one pint from Larry. Their bloodtypes cross matched."

The tourniquet had been taken off Thai Nong's arm, the stump bandaged.

"I clamped off the heavy bleeders and pressure bandaged the entire mess. But it won't hold forever."

"Can he hold on for at least twenty-four hours?" I asked.

"He could probably live for weeks, unless he gets an infection, which is very possible. But the arm would never heal without proper medical attention."

"How are you doing?" I asked the POW who was giving blood. The other prisoner was sitting on the edge of his cot.

"We're free now, aren't we?" he said.

"The camp is ours," I said. "And in about eighteen hours we're going to be heading out."

Sister Therese clamped off the flow of blood, then deftly removed the needle from the POW's arm, covering the puncture with a piece of cotton and tape.

The prisoner started to sit up, but she pushed him back.

"Oh no you don't," she said. "You're staying right here until it's time for us to leave."

He didn't struggle much, and the other POW

looked from him to me.

"Are we really getting out of here, sir?"

"You better believe it," I said.

He smiled. "That'll be nice."

I turned back to Sister Therese who had removed the needle from Thai Nong's arm.

"How soon before he wakes up?"

"I don't know," she said. "There are stimulants here that would bring him around, but they would be very hard on his heart. It would be too dangerous to administer them in his present condition."

"We won't use them now, but get them ready. We may need him awake at a moment's notice."

She nodded then glanced toward the door. "It was bad out there, wasn't it?" she said.

"Yes it was."

She turned to look at me again. "I can't blame them . . . God help me."

I got up from the cot and came around to her. "How did you come to be here?"

"I worked with a missionary medical unit here and in Laos and Thailand," she said. "We were associated with the monastery at Tirlemont. It's near Brussels."

"Then you must know Father Josef?"

"Josef Van der Woort?" she asked.

I nodded.

She smiled. "He is my brother," she said, and the surprise must have shown on my face. "Do you know him?"

"He's here," I said.

She looked wildly around. "Here?"

"He brought me from Thailand. He's just outside the camp now. He'll be coming in at five."

"Josef is here, in Vietnam? Dear God."

She nearly collapsed, and I had to help her to one of the cots where she sat down, tears streaming from her eyes.

"Josef here? What will he think? What will he say when he finds out what has happened to me?"

"He need never know, Sister Therese," I said gently.

"He *will* know," she insisted. "All he will have to do is look at me and he will know."

"Then he will understand," I said. "And forgive."

Colonel Powell came into the dispensary. "We've got the communications and resupply routines," he said excitedly, but then he stopped.

I got up. "Are we going to need Thai Nong this morning?"

"No," Powell said, but he was looking at Sister Therese. "He calls Hanoi every afternoon around 1500 hours."

"Good," I said, turning to the nun. "Keep him under until noon then. That'll give us three hours to convince him to cooperate."

"Are you all right?" Powell asked her.

She got up and managed a slight smile. "Just fine, Colonel. Do any of your people need medical attention?"

"Not at the moment."

"Sometime over the next few hours I want everyone in here, one by one, for vitamin shots. This place is loaded with complex vitamins and energy boosters."

"That stuff has a short shelf life, hasn't it?" I asked.

Sister Therese looked at me and nodded.

"Have any of you been given such injections recently?"

"No," Powell said. "What are you getting at?"

"What was contained in the three trucks that showed up last night?"

"Food. There's a hell of a big pile of it in one of the storage rooms."

"Christ," I said absently.

"What is it?" Powell asked.

"Don't you see? They shipped all this stuff in here because they were planning on feeding it to you and your people. They wanted to build up your strength as rapidly as possible."

"But why . . ." Powell started.

"Because they were planning on beginning negotiations for your release."

"Then it's true?" Powell said.

"What's true?"

"That we lost the war? Saigon fell?"

I nodded.

"They told us that, but we didn't believe it. None of us believed it. And now they'll be demanding reparations payments."

"Something like that," I said.

"No," Powell stated flatly. "No way in hell are we going to allow our government to be held up under threat of us as hostages. We're definitely getting the hell out of here, dead or alive."

"It would be a lot safer if we remained here and simply told Hanoi we were in command. They'd begin negotiations immediately."

"No way," Powell said shaking his head. "No way in hell."

I studied the man for a long moment.

"We're free now, Carter," he said. "Don't you see that we'd rather die here than give it up?"

I glanced at Sister Therese.

"I agree with Colonel Powell," she said.

"I was hoping you'd feel that way," I said. "But we've got a lot of work to do before we get out of here."

"The clean up and burial detail is already at it."

"Fine," I said. "We're going to need weapons and ammunition, food and water, and transportation."

Father Josef had planned on transporting the POWs across Vietnam under the disguise of Vietnamese troops on maneuver. But without live Vietnamese soldiers, the ruse would be impossible. Another idea was forming in my mind instead. It was far-fetched. But possible. Just possible.

The camp kitchen had been opened, and some of the food that had been brought in on the three trucks had been prepared.

As the various work details throughout the camp finished with one project or another, the POWs would wander into the kitchen for a hot meal.

The burial and cleanup crews had completed their grisly task, and only the presence of the graves behind the administration building gave evidence to the fact that forty-seven Vietnamese soldiers had been slaughtered here.

All the weapons from the well-stocked armory had been brought out and neatly stacked on the assembly field for instant use.

As I had suspected would be the case, there was a complete supply of American military uniforms in the supply depot.

The Vietnamese had definitely planned on beginning their negotiations. Included in the discussions would be the authorization of a Red Cross inspection of this camp. When that came about, all the POWs would be well fed and dressed in their uniforms.

In groups of five then, I had the POWs use the large bathroom in Thai Nong's quarters to bathe, shave, and then dress in the clean khakis. But first I had them remove all insignia of rank and military unit.

We had been too busy for me to explain to Powell and his officers exactly what I had in mind, but no one questioned my orders. They were all content to be free, and to be finally working as a unit.

Our last requirement was the vehicles to transport us. I had come from the kitchen and was heading across the compound to find out from Powell if any of his people were mechanics, when the tower guard on the front wall shouted down that someone was coming up the road.

For an instant everything in the compound stopped, but then two dozen men all raced toward the weapons.

"Wait!" I shouted. "Hold up!" I raced to the main gate.

"It's the priest," the tower guard called down.

"Alone?" I shouted up.

"Yes, sir."

"All right, people, back to work. Everything is okay."

Colonel Powell had come out of the supply depot, and he headed across to me at the main gate. "You heard the man, back to work."

Gradually everyone turned back to what they had been doing, and I opened the latch which had been unlocked earlier and swung the tall, bamboo gate inward on its huge hinges.

Father Josef stood about twenty feet up the road, and when he saw that it was me, he slowly crossed himself and then came the rest of the way.

"Any casualties?" he asked.

"None on our side," I said.

He came through the gate, and I closed and re-latched it. "Father Josef, Colonel Gary Powell, senior POW officer."

The two men shook hands. Then Father Josef stepped past him and looked across the camp.

"How about the Vietnamese guards?" he asked.

"They're all dead, Father," Powell said. "There was no other way."

Father Josef turned back to look at him. He shook his head sadly. "No, I suppose there wasn't."

For a moment the three of us were silent, each with his own thoughts, until I finally stepped forward.

"Give us half an hour, Colonel, and then we'll meet with you and your officers in the dining hall."

Powell nodded. "Thank you for coming, Father," he said, and he turned on his heel and strode back across the compound.

"There is someone here who wants to see you," I said gently.

Father Josef turned to look at me. "Someone who knows me?"

"Sister Therese," I said.

The play of emotions across the man's face was so intense it was almost frightening. "Therese . . ."

"She's unharmed and in good spirits," I said.

"Where?" he croaked.

"The dispensary. I'll take you."

"I didn't know," he said, as we headed back across the compound.

He was carrying his pack in his hand, and at the dispensary door I took it from him.

"She's inside," I said. "Come over to the dining hall in about a half hour. I've got an idea how we can get out of here."

He nodded, but I didn't think he heard me. He opened the door and went inside.

I hesitated there for a moment, then turned and went across to the dining hall, where I put Father Josef's pack down, got myself a cup of coffee and lit myself a cigarette.

It was a few minutes after five o'clock, and it would be light soon. In a couple of hours the normal duty day would begin down at command headquarters in Hanoi.

There had been nothing in the communications logs about non-scheduled contacts with Hanoi, or with the military installation at Yen Minh just a few miles away from us.

Colonel Powell had stationed two of his men who spoke near perfect Vietnamese at the radio and telephone. But if they actually had to talk to someone down in Hanoi, I didn't think they would be able to pull it off.

Thai Nong himself was the only one who could buy us time. And there was a good possibility he would refuse.

We had the camp, but now our real troubles were just about to begin.

NINE

"We'll be traveling as a Red Cross convoy," I said from the end of the long table.

Colonel Powell and six of his officers had assembled in the dining hall. Father Josef was seated at the opposite end of the table from me, his mood subdued, his complexion a pasty white. There was no doubt that he knew exactly what had happened with his sister all these years.

We had been talking now for nearly a half hour, and so far we had covered the communications schedule with Hanoi, Thai Nong's recovery and the probability that he could be made to cooperate, as well as the number and type of available vehicles.

Besides the three resupply trucks which had shown up yesterday, there were three other canvas-covered transport trucks and two jeeps with military markings.

It would be a tight fit, but I figured we could all get into the vehicles. Everyone would be armed, and at the tailgate of each truck would be a pair of machine gunners. The radioman would be in the lead jeep monitoring the Vietnamese military channels.

"How about red paint?" I asked.

"There should be some in supply," Powell said.

"I want red crosses painted on all the vehicles, on the doors as well as on the canvas sides."

"Soon as we're done here I'll get my people on it. Shouldn't take more than an hour."

"Any questions then?" I asked.

There were none.

I looked at my watch. It was a few minutes after six. "We'll leave as soon as Thai Nong makes his three o'clock scheduled call to Hanoi."

Father Josef sat forward at that and shook his head. "That'll give you only a twenty-four-hour head start," he said. "If you left within the hour, you would have an extra eight hours."

"We can't leave until Thai Nong makes his call to Hanoi."

"Oh yes you can," Father Josef said. "I'll stay here with him. As soon as he makes his call, I'll get out of here. Back the same way we came."

"You wouldn't have a chance . . ." I started, but he cut me off.

"Don't talk so foolish, Nick. I got you in here, and I can get myself back out. I've been doing it for more than twenty years."

I didn't want to agree with him, and yet what he was saying made a lot of sense. If we did leave within the next hour or so, it would be late at night when we came to the Laotian border. Our chances of bluffing our way across would be much greater.

Some of Powell's men, using documents from Thai Nong's office, were making up travel orders for us, authorizing our passage into Laos. The sooner we started, the greater our chances would be.

"You understand Thai Nong may not want to cooperate with you," I said.

Father Josef looked me directly in the eye. "He will cooperate with us."

"Us?"

"Sister Therese has agreed to remain behind with me. Together we will make sure that Thai Nong lives long enough to make his schedule, and that he actually calls his headquarters."

A silence descended upon the dining hall. Everyone knew what the next question was going to be.

"And afterwards?" I asked it.

"Sister Therese and I leave."

"No, Father, I mean what about Thai Nong. What will you do about him?"

Father Josef didn't say a thing.

"He's too dangerous a man to be left alive," Colonel Powell said. "Even if you destroyed the radio equipment, he would find some way of communicating with the barracks at Yen Minh. Hell, he'd just have to start a fire, and someone would come to investigate."

"We could tie him up. Confine him somehow," Father Josef said.

"And if he got loose?" Powell snapped.

"What do you suggest?" Father Josef asked me.

"He'll have to be killed and his body buried. Afterwards, the communications equipment will have to be destroyed so that even if someone does pay an unexpected visit to the camp, it will take them a while to figure out what happened, and even longer to sound the alarm."

Sister Therese had come from the dispensary and stood now in the doorway listening to us.

"It will be done," she said softly.

Colonel Powell turned to look her way. Father Josef did not look around.

"We can leave one of our people behind," Powell offered. "I'm sure we could get a volunteer."

"No," Sister Therese said sharply. "If just one of you is left behind, it would defeat the entire operation. Father Josef and I will manage here. When we're finished, we'll wait until dark and then slip away. Won't we Josef?"

Father Josef still didn't turn around, but he nodded. "We'll do it," he said softly.

I debated another long moment, but I knew he was right. We were going to have to leave now.

"All right," I said. There was a sigh of relief around the table from Powell and his people. "Let's get the red crosses painted and the trucks loaded. We leave at 0730 sharp." I got to my feet.

"How about road maps!" Father Josef asked, getting up.

"In the orderly room," Powell said.

"Have one of your people bring them over here on the double."

Powell nodded, and he and his officers filed out of the dining hall, but first each of them went up to Father Josef and shook his hand.

Sister Therese came the rest of the way in after the others had left, and the three of us sat down together at one end of the long table.

"He probably won't cooperate with you," I said. "At least not without persuasion."

Father Josef and Sister Therese looked at each other.

"We know that," he said. "We discussed what could be done."

"And?"

He looked at me. "Sister Therese knows what to do. We will manage."

"We can all stay," I said impulsively.

"No," Father Josef shook his head. "As soon as they bring the maps over, I'll show you the route to take that will allow you to avoid most of the larger towns."

"How about the border crossing?"

"You'll go across at Muong Va, where we tried before. I don't think they'll be expecting anyone to come across there so soon after Father Lars."

Once again I debated with myself, this time over whether I should tell him about the fail-safe Sondra and I had worked out. But I decided against it. If something went wrong here, and Father Josef and Sister Therese were captured alive, that information could be extracted from them.

One of Colonel Powell's officers showed up a minute later with several maps. He handed them to me and left.

We spread them out on the table, and Father Josef and I hunched over them.

"I'm going back to see how Thai Nong is doing," Sister Therese said.

I looked up. "When we're ready to go, I'll stop by to say goodbye."

She managed a slight smile. "Thank you, Mr. Carter, for what you are doing," she said, and then she was gone.

Father Josef wanted to say something, I could see it in his expression, but he shook his head and turned his attention to the maps.

Initially we would take the highway toward Hanoi, but about fifty miles south of the camp, well below the city of Ha Giang, we would cut west on a series of secondary roads that would eventually take us across the Red and then Black Rivers which flowed down out of China.

Beyond Lai Chau, there were no other cities for the next thirty miles to the Laotian border near Muong Va.

Father Josef looked up. "Crossing the border is going to be your first major hurdle. You won't have too much trouble from the Laotians, I don't think. At least not at first. You'll present your travel papers showing your destination is the capital, Luang Prabang. But you'll head directly west. It's two hundred miles straight across to Thailand."

"What about the Vietnamese border guards near Muong Va?" I asked.

"That will be your trouble spot. I can't tell you what the best course of action will be. They may simply allow you to pass into Laos, or they might stop you and search the trucks."

"In which case we'd be in trouble."

Father Josef nodded. "If by then they've found out what happened here, you'd also be in trouble."

I knew then what we would have to do at the border, and Father Josef knew it as well, but it would be left unspoken between us.

"At the Thailand border, you're going to have to crash your way through," he said. "I'd suggest that a few miles before the border you radio ahead to the Thai military at Chiang Rai and let them know you're coming. It'll alert everyone, but at least you'll only have to fight the Laotian troops and not the Thai army as well."

I sat back and lit one of the cigarettes I had lifted from Thai Nong's quarters. I inhaled deeply and blew out the smoke slowly.

"What are our chances of making it back to Thailand?"

Father Josef studied me a moment. "The chances that everyone of you will make it back in one piece are next to nothing. But the chances that at least some of you will make it are very good." He hung his head. "It's the best I can do."

I reached out and touched his arm. "Thank you, Father, for your help and for your honesty."

We were ready to leave the camp at seven-thirty that morning. The day was already warm with the rising sun. The POWs were crammed into the six trucks and two jeeps, all of them dressed in crisp new uniforms. They had all bathed, shaved, eaten well, and then were pumped full of vitamin complexes.

All of us were armed; we carried spare ammunition, spare fuel, and plenty of food. Although everyone understood the extreme danger of what we were going to try, and that it was probable that many of us would not make it home, their spirits were high. As of that moment they were a fighting unit of the United States military. They were deep in enemy territory, but they were free men and women.

Colonel Thai Nong was doing fine, although he was still unconscious. As soon as he made his three o'clock communications schedule with Hanoi, Father Josef and Sister Therese would make ready for their own escape.

"Good luck," I said to them.

We stood around the lead jeep, the engine running, the radio on but silent.

Sister Therese kissed me on the cheek. "God bless," she said.

I shook Father Josef's hand.

"God bless you, son," he said. "When this is all over, I want you to come to Tirlemont to see me. We will have a drink together."

"You're leaving Thailand?"

He nodded. "My usefulness is done here now. It is time for me to return home and rest."

I smiled. "I like cognac," I said.

"The abbey has a fine cellar."

I climbed in the jeep beside Powell, and Father Josef hurried ahead to open the main gate.

As we took off slowly across the compound, I looked back, but Sister Therese had already gone into the dispensary, and then we were passing through the gate, and I waved at Father Josef.

Colonel Powell and I were in the back seat of the lead jeep. One of the POWs was driving, and Captain Phil Anderson, the radioman, was in the passenger seat with the radio gear.

"Anything out of that box yet, Phil?" Powell asked after we had gone a couple of miles.

Phil looked back. "Just some routine traffic from the Missile Base back at Yen Minh."

"All right, keep a close ear to it."

"Yes, sir."

The highway we were traveling along was narrow but well maintained, and gradually we picked up the pace, the six trucks and rear jeep maintaining a tight formation behind us.

The farther we went, the more I could see that Powell's spirits were rising. He was even grinning.

Driving like this on a paved highway and on a lovely morning, war and fighting seemed a long way off. It was almost a secure feeling that nothing bad could happen to us as long as we could continue this way.

We all knew better, but for a little while it was pleasant to think that we were just out for a peaceful morning's drive.

The highway, hacked out of the lush green forest, ran fairly straight south, and after an hour and a half of driving we began looking for the turnoff to the secondary road that Father Josef had pointed out on the map.

So far we had encountered no one on the highway, and I was beginning to hope that we would make it to the smaller road where there would be less chance of running into official traffic without incident. But coming over the crest of a hill, that hope was shattered.

Below us, about a half mile farther down the road, some kind of military maneuvers were taking place. Jeeps, trucks, halftracks, and even a few tanks were streaming out of the forests to the west, crossing the road and pulling up in formation a few hundred yards off the road in a clearing to the east.

A pair of jeeps had been pulled up on the highway, their blue lights flashing, as a half dozen soldiers directed traffic.

We had been spotted coming over the hill, so it was too late for us to stop, although the driver instinctively slowed down.

"Red two," I said to the radio operator.

He bent down, put a walkie-talkie to his mouth, and spoke softly into it. "Red two. Red two."

The squad leaders in the six trucks and other jeeps were equipped with walkie-talkies. Red two was our signal that we were in the presence of an armed enemy, but to keep low. Red one was the signal to come out shooting. I hoped to hell we didn't need it this soon.

As we approached the roadblock, one of the tanks in the field swung around so that its main gun was pointed in our general direction. Sweat began to roll down between my shoulder blades.

Our weapons were under the seats, and Powell was rigidly gripping the metal seat frame.

"Easy, Colonel," I said softly. He glanced over at me.

We pulled up about ten feet from the passing column, and two of the soldiers, their weapons at the ready, came up the road to us. The other four soldiers, their weapons at the ready as well, held back and watched.

"Your papers," one of the soldiers said in Vietnamese.

We all reached for the travel documents Powell's men had made for us, and the soldiers brought their weapons up.

We slowly took out our papers and handed them across.

One of the soldiers took the papers and quickly looked them over while the other watched us. When he was finished, he looked directly at Powell and me and said something I couldn't quite catch.

"Dien Bien Phu," Powell said. And then he snapped something else in rapid-fire Vietnamese.

The soldiers both stiffened, and I almost reached for my Luger, but then Powell snapped something else.

The soldiers looked at each other, then back at the column still crossing the road.

Powell said something else, and finally the soldiers handed back our papers, saluted, then went back to where the column was moving and stopped it.

"Let's get the hell out of here while we still have the chance," Powell hissed.

The driver put the jeep in gear and we headed down the road past the soldiers and the waiting column.

I leaned forward, and in the rearview mirror I could see our trucks passing the soldiers one by one. Finally the rear jeep passed, and moments later the soldiers waved their own column to continue across the road.

Within a couple of minutes we had lost sight of the unit and had found our secondary road. We turned off on the dirt track which headed almost directly west toward the Laotian border.

The walkie-talkies we were using had all been re-tuned off their regular channels so that we could use them without fear that Vietnamese radio monitors would pick up our signals.

"You can relax back there now," the radio operator said into his walkie-talkie.

"What the hell happened out there?" one of the squad leaders radioed.

"We passed a VC column on manuevers," Phil said.

"We should have blown them away."

Powell reached forward and grabbed the walkie-talkie. "All right you guys, listen up. We're no longer at war with the Republic of North Vietnam. Get that into your heads and keep it there." He paused a moment. "Besides, they had us outnumbered and outgunned . . . I saw at least three medium duty S10 tanks. You want to go up against them with your pop guns?"

There was no reply. Powell handed the walkie-talkie back, then sighed deeply. "That was goddamned close back there, Carter."

"What the hell did you say to them?" I asked.

He laughed. "He knew we were a Red Cross unit, of course, but he had never seen such a large one. I told him that Laotian refugee children were coming across the border near Dien Bien Phu, and we were being sent down there to feed them."

I looked at him incredulously. "And he believed you?"

"I told him the Laotian incursion was top secret. He backed way off."

I had to laugh too. No one in his right mind would have believed such a story, but the soldiers back there had, and that's all that counted. The story would not work again, however. That would be asking too much.

Through the remainder of the morning and well into the afternoon, we ground our way along the narrow dirt track that was only slightly better than the narrow roads we had traveled in northern Thailand.

We stopped around noon and again around four in the afternoon to refuel the vehicles, but we ate our meals of American C and K rations on the run.

The rice fields of Vietnam were far to our south, so the territory that we were traveling through was mostly forest country. A number of times we passed through small villages, and in a couple of them the villagers came running when they saw the Red Cross markings. But when we passed, they went dejectedly back to their work.

A number of times we passed woodsmen chopping downed trees for firewood.

But no one paid us much attention once it was clear that we were not stopping.

Around seven in the evening we came to the outskirts of Lai Chau, which was a town of at least five thousand. We could see a few dim lights from the city to our north.

"It'll be too risky for us to go through the town," I said.

Laos was only thirty miles away, and Thailand less than two hundred and fifty miles farther. We were getting close. But our first large hurdle was coming up. I didn't want to risk attracting any attention this early.

From the maps we had brought with us, I could see that there were a number of minor roads, farm roads mostly, that skirted the town to the south and then connected with the main east-west highway farther to the west just before the Laotian border.

"There may be impassable spots on some of those roads," Powell said.

"I think we're going to have to take that chance," I said. "It'll be safer than going through Lai Chau."

Powell thought a moment, then looked at me and smiled. "It's hard to make any kind of a decision after ten years of other people making decisions for you."

"We've got to get to the border with no attention," I said. "We'll have to take out the Vietnamese border guards, but without alerting the Laotian people."

"Then let's do it, Nick," he said. He smiled again. "This business of being free is addictive."

"We're not there yet, Gary, but we're getting close."

TEN

It was dark, and we were all bone weary by the time we pulled up on the dirt track a couple of miles from the Laotian border.

"Get the squad leaders up here," I said to the radio operator, and then I turned to Powell. "We go on foot from here."

"We going to take out the border guards?"

I nodded. "It's the only way. They won't let us across, but with the new papers your people made for us, I don't think we'll have any trouble on the other side."

"Unless they decide to search the trucks."

"That's a possibility that we'll have to be ready for." I climbed out of the jeep and lit myself a cigarette as Powell's officers came up from the back of the column.

The night sky was overcast, the jungle pitch black. We had driven for the past five miles without headlights. Now in the dark, the only sounds that could be heard were the night insects and the gentle ticking of the cooling engines. I had a deepening sense of claustrophobia. It seemed as if the entire country was pressing down on me.

Powell had gotten out of the jeep, and he came

around to my side with the others.

"Why did we stop?" one of the officers asked.

I came out of my thoughts and looked up. "We're just a mile or so from the Laotian border," I said.

They all glanced up the road as if they could see what lay ahead.

"I have no idea what the situation is there, so I'm going the rest of the way on foot to find out. I want four people with me."

All of them stepped forward.

"No," I said sharply. "None of you are coming. If anything goes wrong, you're going to have to be here to figure out what the hell you'll do next. I want four of your strongest people. Night fighters. Men who know how to use a knife. We're going to have to take out the border post with absolutely no noise."

They had been cooped up in the trucks for fourteen hours now, and I could see that they were itching for some action. But they were good soldiers, and they all nodded and headed back to their trucks.

I took Powell aside, and we walked twenty-five yards farther up the road so that we were out of earshot of the driver and radioman in our jeep.

"I want you to listen closely now, Gary, because your life and the lives of your people may depend upon what I'm about to tell you."

Powell glanced back at the column. "You're not sure we're going to get across here."

"That's right," I said. "When Father Josef and I came across from Thailand, it was our plan to enter Vietnam at this point. Or very near here. We had another priest with us, Father Lars."

Quickly I told him what had happened in the mine field, and how Father Josef and I had struck north up into the mountains and across to China.

"They may be ready for another incident here, although Father Josef said he didn't think so. It's his belief that the Laotians are disorganized, and we should get through without too much trouble."

"But you think differently?"

"I think it's a distinct possibility that the Laotians may have beefed up their border forces here. If that's the case, we won't get through."

"Then we're stuck."

"Not quite. There is a fail-safe. A last ditch possibility for you."

"You sound less sure of that than you do of our chances of getting across here."

"I am. And even if you were successful in reaching the fail-safe, there could be political repercussions that could very easily escalate into another war out here."

"If it's a choice between that or surrender . . ." Powell started.

"I'm not going to ask you to make that choice. But you'll have to know the entire operation."

"I don't expect you want me to tell the others, in case we do get captured."

"That's right," I said. "If the Vietnamese found out about this, there would be a number of people who wouldn't have a chance."

Powell nodded, and step by step I went through the fail-safe operational plan that Sondra and I had worked out back in Brussels.

When I was finished, Powell's eyes looked at me in disbelief.

"Haiphong," he said. "That's crazy."

"Probably. But it could very well be our only way out of here."

"I hope the hell not."

"Me too," I said.

Four men had come up from the rear of the column, and they waited now by the lead jeep. I motioned them forward, and Powell shook my hand.

"Good luck," he said.

"Thanks. But if you hear any gunshots, turn these trucks around and get the hell out of here." I turned to the other four, who were armed with knives. "There's a Vietnamese border post about two miles up the road. It's separated from the Laotian border post by an open field that's a hundred yards across."

They said nothing, but they were obviously ready.

"We've got to take out the border patrol on this side without alerting the Laotians. If anything happens, get your asses back here immediately. Clear?"

"Yes, sir," they all said.

"Then let's do it," I said. "Have your people get some rest," I said to Powell. "Meanwhile, you'd better take a close look at the maps, just in case."

Powell nodded, and I turned and headed down the dirt road, the four POWs right behind me.

Within a few minutes we were out of sight of the others, and we continued at a fast pace, listening for sounds ahead of us as we went.

Fifteen minutes later we came to the paved highway that ran from Lai Chau in Vietnam to Muong Va and beyond, in Laos.

A few hundred yards down the highway, the border crossing area was lit up by strong lights. A striped barrier was stretched across the highway, and on the left side of the road was a guard hut with several large windows.

From where we crouched in the darkness just off the highway, we could see two soldiers in the guard hut, but no one else. A jeep was parked to one side.

Beyond the Vietnamese border post, a hundred yards farther down the highway, was a similar set up, although at this distance we could not make out the guards themselves.

There were probably other similar posts strung at intervals all along the border, with patrols traveling between them.

We'd have to take the patrol out first, and then the highway post.

We fell back about a quarter mile down the dirt road, then headed through the forest directly toward the border, taking extreme care to make absolutely no noise.

Within a few minutes we had come to the clearing that separated the two countries. There were no fences and no barbed wire. All that was unnecessary because the entire area was mined.

The five of us lay stretched out on the forest floor watching the border and waiting for the patrol to come by. I had no idea how long we would have to wait, but I expected it wouldn't be too long.

Within a half an hour we spotted the lone soldier coming up from the south, heading toward the highway post.

I took out my stiletto and waited as the man slowly made his way along the border, finally passing our position. As he passed I crawled out from the darkness. When I was directly behind the soldier, but about twenty-five yards back, I got up in a half crouch, and silently raced toward him.

He heard me and spun around, bringing his rifle up while I was still fifteen or twenty feet away.

Without breaking stride, I drew my arm back and flipped the stiletto with every ounce of my strength.

The blade buried itself to the haft in his chest. The soldier grunted in surprise, and stepped back, the rifle falling to the ground.

I was on him a second later, knocking him to the ground and clamping my right hand over his mouth and nose.

He shuddered once and then lay still. His eyes were open and staring sightlessly up at me.

I got up, pulled the stiletto from his chest and wiped the blade on the grass. The four POWs came out of the forest and joined me.

"I thought he had you there, sir," one of them said softly.

I nodded. "So did I," I said. "I want one of you to get into his uniform."

We pulled the body out of the clearing back into the forest, stripped him of his clothes and equipment, and one of the smaller men put the uniform on while the others kept a watch for any other patrols. But none came, and when we were ready I quickly outlined my plan, and we headed out, keeping to the forest, the border clearing to our left.

Nothing had changed at the border post. The jeep was still there, and the two guards were still inside the hut. It looked like they were eating.

Two of the POWs and I got down on our stomachs, crawled out of the forest, and headed slowly and silently across the clearing directly toward the back of the border post.

From time to time we looked up toward the post, and we could see the two guards there. Even if they looked our way, I was sure that they would not be able to spot us out here, because their night vision was ruined by the strong lights up on the highway.

My only concern was that the Laotians would be watching the border post and might spot us. But it was a risk we had to take.

We reached the back of the post a few minutes later without incident. I cut the telephone line with my stiletto, then waved toward the others still back in the forest.

The one dressed in the Vietnamese uniform came out of the forest, down into the clearing, and then headed in plain sight up toward the border post.

As he got closer, he began to slow down and stagger. "Help," he called out in Vietnamese with a weak voice.

At first nothing happened, and he kept coming, calling weakly for help.

But then the guards inside the post began talking excitedly, and we could hear the front door open and close.

The POW in the uniform fell to his knees and then dropped over, his face in the grass.

We were crouched down low behind the building when one of the guards appeared and headed in a dead run toward what he believed was a fallen comrade.

I waited tensely, holding the stiletto tightly in my right hand. This wasn't going to work unless the other guard came around the corner too.

The first guard had just about reached the fallen POW, when the second stepped around the corner of the building, just a few feet away from where I crouched.

I sprang up, grabbed the startled soldier by his collar and jerked him down.

He cried out as I clamped my left hand over his mouth. The first guard spun around and brought his rifle up, but at that moment the fallen POW jumped up and buried his knife in the guard's back.

My man was struggling hard, and with my knee in his back, I yanked his head backwards, his spine breaking with a sickening snap.

The other POW came out of the forest, and as he helped pull the first guard back up to us, we stripped the other guard's uniform off him.

"We've got the post," I said softly as two of the POWs dressed in the guards' uniforms. "We'll stay here while one of you returns to Colonel Powell. Tell him to get up here with the trucks. We're going across immediately."

"Yes, sir," the one POW not dressed in a Vietnamese uniform said, and he turned, hurried across the clearing, and disappeared into the forest.

I eased around the corner of the building and looked down the highway. There was no traffic. No movement whatsoever.

Continuing around the building, I slipped inside, the others joining me a moment later.

A powerful pair of binoculars on a tripod stood in one of the windows facing the Laotian border.

I looked through them. They were focused on the Laotian border post, which in construction was very similar to this one.

There were four border guards in the post, and another two out on the road. One of them was looking directly at me through a pair of binoculars.

We stared at each other like that for a few moments, until he finally lowered his binoculars, said something to the other guard, and then turned and walked down the road.

I followed him with the binoculars until he disappeared into the forest. I could see flashes of light from the area to the right of the road, but then they disappeared.

There was something back there. Every instinct within me told me that there was something wrong. Something very wrong.

I straightened up and looked at the others. The half a dozen guards at the post I could understand. The Laotians may have gotten a little jittery after the explosion along their border when Father Lars had touched off the mine.

But where had the guard gone? Why back into the forest? And what was the meaning of the light flashes I had seen?

I looked through the binoculars again, but nothing had changed. There were four guards in the post, plus the one out on the highway looking this way.

I straightened up again. "I want one of you men to hike back up to the dirt road and wait for Colonel Powell and the others."

"Sir?" one of them said. "Is something wrong over there?"

"I don't know," I said. "Just get up to the dirt road and tell Powell to hold the column there. I don't want them out on the highway just yet. And have him come down here on foot."

"Yes, sir," he said, and he turned to go out the door.

"Don't try to conceal yourself," I said. "Just go out the door and walk down the road."

He looked at me, a strange expression in his face, but then he nodded, went out the door, and headed down the road.

I turned back to the binoculars. The guard out on the road had raised his binoculars, and he was looking this way.

After a couple of moments he lowered his binoculars and hurried across the road into the guard post. I could see him clearly through the windows as he picked up a telephone.

I stepped away from my binoculars. The other two men were staring at me.

"What's going on, sir?"

"I think we've got trouble," I said. "I want one of you to watch the border post across there. I'm going up to meet Powell."

"What is it?"

I was at the door. "I think the goddamned Laotians are over there in force. I think they're getting set to cross the border."

"Jesus Christ," one of them said, and he went to the binoculars.

"If anything happens, if they start across, get the hell out of here. Do you understand?" I said.

"Yes, sir," the one at the binoculars said.

"That's all we need right now is an invasion," the other one said, nervously looking toward the Laotian border post.

Maybe it was exactly what we needed at this moment, I thought as I went out the door and hurried down the highway toward the dirt road a few hundred yards away.

As I walked I could almost feel the Laotian border guard's eyes on my back. I knew they could see me. And I knew they had to be wondering just who the hell I was, dressed in plain khaki.

By the time I turned off the highway and headed down the dirt road, I could hear the sound of Powell and the column moving up. There was no place for them to turn around here, which meant they were going to have to come out onto the highway in plain sight of the Laotians.

The lead jeep appeared out of the darkness a few moments later, the trucks in close formation behind it.

I flagged them down and went around to Powell. "Trouble?" he asked.

"I think so," I said, and I told him exactly what I had seen across the border.

"Christ, do you think it's possible?" he asked.

"Anything is possible out here, Colonel. But I think we'd better get these trucks turned around and head toward Haiphong."

"That's a suicide mission," he said. "If the Laotians are actually mounting an attack on Vietnam, why don't we just give ourselves up to them, and ask for safe passage to Thailand in return for opening the border here."

"The Laotians don't love us anymore than the Vietnamese,' I said. "They'd just gun us down and roll right over us."

Powell took a deep breath and let it out slowly. "What are our chances of making it to Haiphong?"

"Not very good. But if the Laotians are actually coming across here tonight, our chances of surviving here would be even less."

He nodded. "Then we do it."

"All right then," I said. "I'll walk back up to the border post. On my signal I want you to lead the convoy out onto the highway, but turn right, away from the border, and go a couple of miles down the road. When you're out of sight of the border, get turned around, and then haul ass back here. When you show up, we'll come running and go back the same way we came."

"You're banking that their primary objective will be Lai Chau?"

"It's the nearest town of any size," I said. "I think they'll roll right down the main highway." I smiled. "It just might give us enough of a diversion to pull this off."

"I hope the hell you're right, Carter," Powell said.

"So do I," I said. I turned and went back down the dirt road to the highway, then walked briskly back to the border post.

"Is Colonel Powell back there?" one of the POWs asked when I came in.

"He just showed up," I said, crossing over to the binoculars. "Anything going on over there?"

"There's ten of them now," the POW said, moving aside so that I could look.

There were ten armed soldiers, all of them out on the highway now, and all of them heavily armed. There was little doubt in my mind now. They were definitely planning on an attack. The flashes of light I had seen back in the forest were from the main body of troops and vehicles. And by the looks of things they would be coming across very soon.

I went back to the door, and keeping the building between me and the Laotians, waved my arms.

Almost immediately Powell's jeep emerged from the forest out onto the highway, turned to the right, and headed away, followed closely by the six trucks and the rear jeep.

"Watch the border," I said over my shoulder.

"They look excited as hell, sir," the POW at the binoculars said.

"Any mechanized equipment yet?"

"No, sir," he said.

The rear jeep in the column disappeared around a curve, and I went back inside.

"Where the hell did they go?" one of the POWs asked.

"Just out of sight so they can turn around. I think the Laotians are going to come across this border very soon. We're getting the hell out of here."

"Jesus. Where are we going to go?"

"Away from here," I said.

"Here they come!" the man at the binoculars said.

I didn't need to look through the glasses to see the tanks and armored trucks coming out of the woods onto the highway and turning our way.

We had just run out of time.

"The lights," I shouted, unslinging my rifle and throwing open the door. I leaped out onto the highway, brought my rifle up, and snapped off a few shots. At least one of the soldiers on the highway went down before the others scattered.

The first answering rounds came our way when the lights went out.

"Get the hell out of there," I shouted, racing in

a zigzag pattern down the highway.

The two POWs came out of the guard post in a dead run, and we had gotten less than fifty yards when an artillery round came in from one of the tanks, scoring a direct hit on the post.

If Powell and the convoy didn't get back to the dirt road before the tanks moved across the border, we would be cut off from our escape route.

Behind me I could hear the tanks and other vehicles beginning to roll over the rattle of small arms and machine gun fire.

"For Christ's sake, come on, Powell."

As if in answer, the column appeared around the curve, and we reached the dirt road about the same time.

"Move," I shouted, leaping into the jeep. The other two POWs climbed aboard the first truck in line as a second and third artillery round came in, striking less than fifty yards behind us.

"Move! Move! Move!" our radioman shouted into the walkie-talkies, and we careened around the corner and headed down the dirt road as fast as the jeep would move, while behind us more artillery rounds came in.

ELEVEN

Within a couple of minutes the firing behind us had died down. The Laotians had gotten a good look at the Red Cross markings on our vehicles, and they probably figured our people dressed as border guards had simply deserted their post and left with the harmless convoy.

My immediate concern was that the road we were on paralleled the Laotian border for several miles. If the Laotians were attacking across the border from more than one point, it was still possible that we could become involved in the fight.

We were doing around fifty miles per hour down the rough, narrow dirt road, and behind us, the trucks were beginning to spread out.

I sat forward and had to shout over the noise in order for the radioman, Phil, to hear me. "Radio the rear jeep and make sure we're intact."

Phil nodded and brought the walkie-talkie to his lips, but I could not hear what he was saying. After a moment he turned around and gave me the thumbs up sign.

"Scan the Vietnamese military frequencies," I shouted. "We have to know how they're reacting to the attack."

145

"If we go directly to Haiphong, we'll be there in broad daylight," Powell shouted in my ear.

I nodded. "We'll have to take our chances. We can't hang around here. And every hour we spend out on the road increases our risk of capture. By three, if Thai Nong doesn't check in by phone with Hanoi, they'll know we're gone anyway. We have to be in Haiphong long before that."

"Are you sure about the fail-safe, Carter?"

"It doesn't matter, does it?" I shouted. "We can't stay here. And there's no where else to go."

Powell nodded and sank back in his seat.

Ten minutes later, as the dirt road turned east away from the border, the radioman turned in his seat.

"The garrison at Lai Chau is under attack," he shouted.

"What are they doing about it?" I shouted.

"Air strikes have been ordered out of Hoa Binh as far as I can tell."

"Are they attacking anywhere else?"

Phil shook his head. "I don't know," he shouted. "There's too much conflicting traffic. No one seems to know what the hell is going on yet."

"Good. Let's hope it stays that way a little while longer."

We passed well south of Lai Chau, picking up the highway we had come down on. We remained on that for about twenty miles and then turned southeast on one of the main highways that led toward Hanoi.

There was some traffic, but all of it was military and heading west toward the trouble at the border and at Lai Chau. No one paid us the slightest attention.

By three A.M., we were a hundred miles away from the border, and although we were all dead tired, I could see that Powell and the others were once again feeling good about our chances.

Radio traffic on the Vietnamese military channels had completely died off, and I assumed they had imposed radio silence or they had switched to alternate frequencies that our radio was unable to pick up.

At least two squadrons of jet fighters had passed overhead in the night, and shortly after three we could see the lights of half a dozen heavy transport aircraft heading west.

Mile by mile we continued to the southeast, finally crossing the Red River around six in the morning.

At this point we were less than fifty miles northwest of Hanoi, and we stopped to refuel with the remainder of our gas.

We were in the rice paddies of central North Vietnam, and we pulled off the highway onto a wide, gravelly area littered with raw rice and husks and a shaky wooden platform with ramps at both ends.

"They load their rice crop aboard the transport trucks from places like this," Powell said tiredly. His eyes were red rimmed and puffy, and his speech was slurred.

We got out and stretched our legs as men from each of the vehicles got out to empty the jerry cans of gasoline into the truck and jeep tanks.

In the fields around us, we could see workers slogging through the knee-deep mud and water to tend their fields.

The sky was still overcast, the weather very

muggy, and it looked as if it would rain very soon.

"Tell the squad leaders to keep their people in the trucks," I told the radioman.

He looked at me bleary-eyed, and then got on the walkie-talkie and relayed my orders.

"How far?" Powell asked me.

I looked at him. "A little more than a hundred miles," I said. "Three hours at best." I looked at my watch. It was a few minutes after six A.M. "We should be there sometime before ten."

"I don't know if we're going to make it, Nick," he said.

"Ten years of shit, and you can't go another three hours?" I snapped.

Powell looked at me with a pained expression, and my heart went out to him. We were so close, and yet the worst part was still to come. I had no idea what it was going to be like skirting Hanoi, or what we would find when—and if—we finally reached the seaport city of Haiphong.

There were a quarter of a million people in the city and nearly one million people in the district. We would have to go directly through the heart of the city at the height of the business day.

There were a lot of worrisome variables to consider: how the Laotian attack would affect the Vietnamese military readiness and awareness; the situation at the moment back at the POW camp near Yen Minh; and whether or not Sondra had been successful in setting up the fail-safe we had planned.

"Trouble," Powell said.

I had been staring across the rice paddies, and I spun around.

A military police jeep, its blue light flashing, was coming down the highway from the east. There was a driver and a passenger. The passenger was gesturing toward us as the jeep slowed down.

"Get everyone back in the trucks," I snapped.

"Back in the trucks. Move it!" Powell shouted.

"Red two! Red two!" I shouted at the radioman, who looked around as the jeep pulled off the highway. He keyed the walkie-talkie.

"Red two! Red two!" he barked.

The jeep screeched to a halt ten feet from where Powell and I stood. The driver and passenger, both in military uniform with military police armbands around their right arms, jumped out, bringing their automatic weapons up.

"Good morning," Powell started to say in Vietnamese, when someone from one of the trucks opened fire.

In an instant it seemed as if every POW in the convoy was firing at the two Vietnamese military police who went down in bloody heaps.

"Stop! Stop it!" Powell was screaming.

The firing stopped as quickly as it had begun. Guys were hanging out of the trucks, their weapons in hand, sheepish looks on their faces.

"Finish the refueling," I shouted, racing toward the fallen soldiers.

They were both dead, their bodies riddled with bullets. We would have to get the hell out of here and now.

Powell helped me pull the military police armbands off the bodies.

"We're going to have to take their jeep," I said.

"A military escort?"

"Something like that." I looked up. "I need two of your men who were with me at the border," I shouted. "On the double."

A moment later two of the POWs who had helped me at the border, and who were still dressed in the Vietnamese uniforms, jumped out of one of the trucks and hustled over to us.

"Put these on," I said handing them the armbands. "You're going to drive their jeep. I'll ride with you."

"Yes, sir," they said.

"Get these bodies in the trucks, and let's get the hell out of here," I snapped.

Powell directed four of the POWs to pick up the two bodies. They stuffed them in one of the trucks and then climbed back up themselves.

"Follow us," I snapped. "We'll head around Hanoi, but we're going right through Haiphong. Have your people ready for a *Red One* signal if I open fire. But we're not stopping for anything."

"Right," Powell said. He raced back to his jeep as I jumped into the military police vehicle, its blue light still flashing.

The trucks all started up as we swung around and pulled out onto the highway, and within a couple of minutes we were on the move, racing against certain discovery down to Haiphong and Sondra Kinderman's fail-safe.

Traffic on the highway increased dramatically the farther southeast we pushed, and twenty miles outside of Hanoi, when we turned off the north-south highway so that we could skirt the city to the north, there were a lot of military vehicles on the roads.

None of them paid us any attention, however,

and we continued without incident through the heavily industrialized area, high power lines criss-crossing the skyline, factories spewing their smoke into the heavily overcast sky.

By eight A.M., when it finally began to rain, we had passed well east of Hanoi, skirting Bac Ninh to the south, and we pushed down to the sea and the port city of Haiphong.

A number of worries crossed my mind as we drove, foremost among them, whether or not Sondra had been successful. If we were caught in Haiphong without the fail-safe, there would be no going back, and certainly no escape.

Considering the mood Powell and his people were in at this moment, if we did run into trouble it would turn out to be a blood bath, something I wanted to avoid at all costs.

The countryside became more marshy the closer to Haiphong we came. Rice paddies were interspersed with factories, power plants, and what looked like vast stockpiles of coal, iron ore and other minerals.

About ten miles out of Haiphong, the driver looked over his shoulder and then gestured for me to look back.

I turned around in time to see a military police jeep, its blue light flashing, coming up alongside the convoy.

Besides the driver there were three other soldiers in the jeep, all of them armed with machine guns.

They pulled up alongside us and gestured for us to pull over. They looked ready to fight.

I pulled out my papers from my breast pocket and held them up, shaking my head.

The soldiers in the jeep pointed again for us to pull off the road.

I leaned forward as if to talk to my driver as I reached down and grabbed the Kalashnikov at my feet.

I clicked the safety off, then slumped sideways as I brought the rifle up.

They saw what was happening and started to bring their machine guns up, but it was too late for them. I opened fire, spraying the jeep from left to right.

The driver was hit, his body slamming to the left, and his jeep suddenly swerved that way, hitting the ditch and then flipping over twice before it exploded in a ball of fire.

We crossed three bridges in quick succession, one of them over railroad tracks, and we were in Haiphong. Then we had to slow down for the heavy traffic.

The city was on a large delta island, rivers and canals cutting everywhere. There was a mass of vehicular and pedestrian traffic, all seemingly unaffected by the rain which had turned into a bath-warm downpour.

Even now, so long after the fighting had ceased, many of the buildings in the city were bomb damaged, little more than burned-out shells.

We created a lot of attention, but no one made any move to flag us down or to block our passage as we went directly through the downtown area and finally came to the commercial docks.

There were a mass of warehouses and loading facilities along several long concrete quays.

At least a dozen civilian transport vessels were either tied up at the docks or lay at anchor in the harbor. Two warships, one of them Russian, also

lay at anchor, and there were at least two dozen
Vietnamese naval gunboats also tied up or at anchor.

I spotted the *Karpitz* almost immediately, its
East German Democratic Republic flag snapping
in the brisk wind that had come with the rain.

There were three Vietnamese military police vehicles parked at the ship's boarding ladder, and I
directed my driver to head directly toward them.

A canvas awning had been put up between a
couple of the jeeps, and half a dozen soldiers stood
under it, out of the rain.

They looked up curiously as we pulled to a halt,
and I jumped out, waving my papers.

I hurried back to Powell's jeep.

"This is it?" he asked.

I nodded. "Red one," I said softly.

Powell took a deep breath and let it out slowly as
he glanced over at the soldiers under the awning,
then he nodded at the radio operator, who keyed
the walkie-talkie.

"Red one," he said softly. "Red one."

For a very long, pregnant second or two,
absolutely nothing happened. But then it was as if
a bomb had been placed in the middle of the convoy, the trucks exploding with POWs firing their
weapons even before they hit the dock.

The soldiers under the awning went down without firing a shot.

"The ship!" I shouted. "Get aboard the ship!
They're friends!"

Powell and a couple of his officers began direct-
ing POWs up the gangway as I grabbed a couple of
men and we raced toward the aft bollards where
the ship's docking lines were tied.

We managed to undo the aft two lines and were

racing toward the bow, when the ship's diesels came to life, and sirens began to sound throughout the harbor and city.

Several of the POWs on the gangway went down under fire from the end of the dock, and I spun around in time to see a couple of armored vehicles rumbling out onto the quay.

"Get the lines," I shouted, breaking away and racing back to the military police jeep we had captured north of the city.

It had a fifty caliber machine gun mounted on a rear post. Reaching the jeep I jumped in the back seat and swung the gun around as Powell, seeing what I was attempting to do, jumped in the driver's seat, started the engine and swung the jeep around so that I could just see the armored vehicles coming down the quay.

I opened fire immediately, aiming for the right side track on the lead machine.

The heavy caliber slugs ricochetted off the steel treads, and for several anxious moments I didn't think they were having any effect.

Suddenly, though, the track seemed to snake out from under the armored vehicle, which swung sharply right. The other machine crashed into it.

"Let's go," I shouted jumping out of the jeep and racing toward the ship's boarding ramp.

I thought Powell was right behind me, but when I started up the ramp I looked back in time to see him running back to one of the trucks for a downed POW.

As I stepped down from the ramp, I brought my rifle up and started firing toward the Vietnamese troops coming out of the armored vehicles.

Powell had the POW up on his shoulders and

headed back toward me as the ship began to move away from the dock.

"Powell!" I shouted.

Ten feet from the ramp, Powell was hit in the leg and started to go down. I fired another burst, then tossed down my rifle, leaped to him, and half carried and half dragged him back to the ramp and then up it, the firing intense now from the other POWs along the rails of the ship.

We somehow managed to reach the top and fall onto the deck as the ramp fell away from the moving ship.

A couple of the POWs went down under fire from the dock before the rest of them ducked down below the rail.

"You all right, Powell?" I asked sitting up.

He was grinning. "Just a flesh wound, I think," he said. "Christ. We made it."

"Not yet, we've still got to get out of the harbor to the open sea," I said.

"Nick!" a woman screamed my name.

I turned in time to see Sondra Kinderman coming out of a hatchway just aft.

"Down!" I shouted, as more firing came from the dock.

She ducked down as a line of rounds came in, richochetting off the bulkhead just above her head.

She quickly crawled across to where I was crouched beside Powell and the POW he had carried aboard.

"What the hell are you doing here?" I snapped.

"You made it," she bubbled. "You actually made it."

"Are there any medics aboard?"

She nodded, looking over at the several POWs

who had been hit. "Below," she said. "We have a doctor and three nurses."

"Listen up you guys," I shouted.

They all looked my way.

"Squad leaders, I want you to get your people below. There's medical help aboard. When you have your people taken care of, I'll need a head count on the bridge."

Powell was cradling the head of the POW he had carried aboard. The man had taken at least a half dozen hits. His body was blood soaked. He was obviously dead.

"He died a free man, Nick," Powell said. "No one had to bargain for him. He wasn't used as a hostage."

"He got this far, Gary," I said. "We'll get him the rest of the way home."

A couple of the other POWs crawled over and helped Powell with the body.

The firing from the dock had stopped, and we were underway, but we had to move slowly because we were still in a crowded harbor.

We could still hear sirens from the shore, and I expected that it would not be very long before we were challenged either by the Vietnamese gunboats, which I felt we could handle, or by one of the Soviet destroyers in the harbor, which I knew we definitely could *not* handle.

"Let's get up to the bridge," I said.

Sondra looked at me for a long moment. She reached out and caressed my cheek. "You look like hell, Nick," she said softly. "Are you all right?"

"I'll manage," I said.

TWELVE

From the moment I came on the bridge it was evident that we were in serious trouble.

The captain, Ernst Hausmann, was a legitimate East German who had done other work for us before. He was on the radio talking with the Vietnamese harbor officials. Although I was able to catch only bits and pieces of what he was saying, it was clear that the Vietnamese were ordering him back to the dock, and he was violently protesting the fact that his vessel had been fired upon.

When Sondra and I came through the hatch, he glanced at us, rolled his eyes, and mopped his sweaty brow with a dirty handkerchief.

The harbor breakwater exit and lighthouse were dead on the bow about two miles off. To the right of the exit, but well within the breakwater, one of the Soviet destroyers at anchor was sending us light signals, but as far as I could tell they were not making ready to get underway or challenge us with a show of force.

Overhead a pair of helicopters had come from shore, and they were hovering amidships just off our port and starboard sides.

The young helmsman at the wheel kept looking

nervously from the Soviet destroyer back to his captain, and again to the destroyer.

"Steady as she goes," Hausmann said in German, cupping the radio-telephone.

"Aye aye, sir," the young man said, gripping the wheel tighter.

"Did you have any trouble in Naples?" I asked, taking Sondra aside.

She shook her head. "None with the ship. But Hawk either guessed or somehow found out what I was up to, and he called me. I had to tell him everything."

"What'd he say?"

"He thought it was a good idea, Nick. But he made us off load the weaponry."

"All of it?"

She nodded.

Sondra had managed to come up with a couple of French made rocket launching units, which we had planned on using if all else failed. This ship was virtually defenseless, except for the weapons the POWs had brought aboard with them.

The captain slammed the radio-telephone handset down on its cradle. *"Verdammt,"* he swore, and he turned to look at us.

"What did they say?" I asked in German.

He looked at me, his eyes narrow. "They say for me to turn this ship around, give back what we have taken, and we will be allowed to leave unmolested."

"And if you do not comply?"

"They will consider it an act of war," he said. He turned to his helmsman. "Come about sharply," he snapped.

"No," I shouted.

"This is my ship!" Hausmann roared. "I won't have it sunk out from under me for any reason. We go back!"

The helmsman started to turn the big wheel to the starboard. I pulled out my Luger.

"Bring us back on course, or I will shoot you both now."

Hausmann's complexion turned a mottled red, and the helmsman's eyes went wide.

"Now!" I shouted, raising the Luger a little higher.

For several seconds we stood like that, the ship slowly swinging to the port, until the captain finally nodded. "Do as he says."

The young helmsman, relieved, brought the ship back on course, the breakwater exit once again dead on the bow.

"I was not informed that we would be transporting people. Criminals," Hausmann said.

"Those criminals, as you call them, Captain, are United States military men and officers who have been held prisoner for ten years or more."

"Prisoners of war?" Hausmann asked incredulously.

I nodded. "Prisoners, but of a war that has long since been settled."

"*Gott in Himmel,*" Hausmann said, running a hand over his hair. He turned and went to the large windows and looked out. "They will not allow us to leave their territorial waters."

"They won't sink us, Captain," I said.

"And why not?" he asked without turning around.

"The political repercussions would be too vast."

Hausmann was silent for a moment. But then he

shook his head. "Then I would suggest, Mein Herr, that you tell your story to the captains of those vessels."

Sondra and I joined him at the windows in time to see the big Vietnamese gunboats surrounding us. There were at least a dozen of them, and from where we stood watching, we could see that their bow and stern guns, as well as their rocket launchers, were manned.

One of them cut directly across our bow, less than fifty yards ahead.

"What do you suggest?" Hausmann said bitterly.

"Full speed ahead!"

"In the harbor?"

"Yes, in the harbor!" I snapped.

The man hesitated. "Prisoners for ten years, you say?"

I nodded.

"Your government knew nothing of their existence?"

"They were on our missing in action lists."

"The bastards," he said. He sighed deeply. "Full speed ahead."

"Full speed ahead, aye aye, sir," the helmsman said, and he rang for the increase. The telegraph was answered, and we could feel the ship's diesels winding up to full scale, the entire ship shuddering with the sudden surge of power.

A second gunboat had just begun to cut across our bow, and it peeled off to the starboard at the last moment to avoid being rammed.

Another of the gunboats fired a shell across our bow seconds later, a geyser of water splashing down on our decks.

The radio-telephone receiver was buzzing angrily.

"Hold it steady," I said. The captain was looking directly into my eyes. I clicked the Luger's safety on and holstered it.

Hausmann nodded. "It doesn't matter now, anyway," he said. "I'm committed."

"Is there a ship's intercom, or some way of talking to the people below?"

The captain nodded toward another handset next to the radio-telephone. I went across to it and thumbed the switch.

"Listen up down there," I said into the handset, and I could hear my amplified voice booming through the ship. "This is Carter. I'm on the bridge. I want every man who is not wounded, or who is not attending the wounded, up on deck, armed, and in plain view. We need a show of force now, and we may have to repel boarders."

We were less than a mile from the harbor exit and closing fast as I repeated the message. The Soviet destroyer had still made no move to weigh anchor and join the chase, although she was still sending us light signals.

One of the gunboats fired another shell across our bow, again splashing water up on our decks, and this time it came a lot closer to actually hitting us.

"That was close," Hausmann said. "I think they mean to sink us if we don't stop."

"We continue," I said grimly. I turned to Sondra. "Did Hawk say anything to you about backing us up?"

"No," she said. "Not a thing."

We were closing fast now on the harbor exit, and

the Vietnamese gunboats were operating closer and closer to us. One mistake on their part, and it was possible that we would ram one of them. If that happened, all hell would break loose.

There wasn't much room in the crowded harbor for any of us to maneuver, but once we got out into the open sea, I felt we could make a run for it.

I stepped out of the bridge for a moment and looked down on deck as the POWs came out to the rail. A few of them looked up, grinned and waved. I waved back.

A hundred or so deeply fatigued men and women, with a collection of light weapons, against at least a dozen heavily armed gunboats.

I shook my head. It wasn't much of a contest. All we had going for us was our will. There wasn't one man or woman down there who would give up now. They were free, and they would either survive, or they would die. Either way, they would remain free.

Getting them out of here, however, without a blood bath was going to be next to impossible.

Back inside the captain stood at one of the windows, a microphone in his hand.

I started to ask him what he was doing, but then I spotted one of the gunboats pulling up and presenting its broadside to us. It was directly in the harbor exit.

"Stand off!" the captain said into the microphone, and his voice greatly amplified boomed from the speakers outside. "Stand off or be rammed!"

The gunboat wallowed in the swells coming through the breakwater, but it gave no indication of moving away from its position as we rapidly closed on it.

"Nick?" Sondra said.

We were close enough now to see a dozen soldiers lining the rail of the ship. They were betting their lives that we would not ram them.

Hausmann was watching me, waiting for me to tell him to stand off.

But then I could hear a noise from outside on the decks of our ship.

Hausmann was about to say something, but I held up a hand to silence him, and we all listened.

It was the POWs. They were shouting something. Something that sounded like a cheer at a football game.

"Go! Go! Go!" They were all chanting the word. They wanted us to ram the gunboat.

We were close now. Fifty yards. And it was too late for us to do anything. Impossible for us to avoid hitting them.

Hausmann hit the ship's whistle, and the deep-throated roar blasted throughout the harbor.

"Brace yourselves!" I shouted.

At the last possible moment, the water at the stern of the gunboat suddenly began to boil, black smoke came from her stack, and she moved away.

Our bow wave, as we passed just feet behind the gunboat, caused the smaller vessel to broach, nearly capsizing, and we were out of the harbor, our bow rising to meet the incoming deep ocean swells.

"Jesus," the captain swore, his face wet with perspiration.

The POWs at the rails were cheering now, as we plowed into the open sea.

"We made it, Nick. My God, we made it," Sondra was shouting and crying.

"Not yet . . ." I started to say, and suddenly one of the gunboats, moving at high speed, passed us on our portside and headed directly out to sea.

"What the hell is he doing?" Haussmann roared.

A second and third gunboat passed us on our portside, and then others were screaming by us on both sides, heading straight out to sea.

Hausmann grabbed a pair of binoculars and peered through them.

I watched through the windows as the gunboats continued way out, finally splitting left and right about two or three miles off our bow.

"Verdammt! Verdammt!" the captain sputtered, and he lowered his binoculars, looked at me, then at the helmsman. "All ahead slow, helmsman."

"What the hell . . ." I started, but Hausmann held the binoculars out to me.

"All ahead slow," he repeated.

As I stepped forward, took the binoculars from Hausmann, and raised them to my eyes, the helmsman said, "Aye aye, sir," and rang for the all ahead slow.

I focused on the gunboats way out ahead of us, and at first I didn't understand what I was seeing. The boats had split left and right and were making a large circle back toward us. As the boats cut through the swells, black objects were being ejected from their fantails, arching high into the sky and falling into the ocean with a small splash.

Suddenly I understood. "Mines?" I asked, lowering the binoculars.

"That's the way I see it," Hausmann said. "They're laying a mine field around us."

Sondra had come forward. "If we try to go through it, and we're sunk, it'll be our fault."

I raised the binoculars again and watched as the gunboats continued around in a huge circle. There was no way possible for us to turn around now and have any chance of getting outside the mine field. They had us effectively boxed in.

The ship's intercom pinged, and Hausmann picked up the handset. "Bridge," he snapped.

He listened for a long moment, then turned to look at me and Sondra, an odd expression on his face.

"What is it?" I asked.

"Carter? Nick Carter?"

I nodded.

He held the handset out to me. "Someone wants to talk to you."

I took the handset from him and put it to my ear. "Carter," I said.

"Carter, this is John Wilson aboard the NSS *Barracuda*."

It was a U.S. nuclear submarine. I knew of the boat, but where the hell was it?

"Listen up, Carter. We're about eight miles southeast of your position. We've sent a radio buoy up so you could receive our transmission."

It was possible it was a ruse. "Who sent you?" I asked.

"David. After he talked to Sondra in Naples."

The Soviets could have had that information. "I need more," I said.

Sondra and Hausmann were looking at me.

"You sonofabitch," the man shouted. "N3. Wilhelmina. Hugo . . ."

I cut him off. No one knew those names. "All

right, captain, I believe you. Now how about getting us the hell out of here?"

There was a pause on the line, and I looked out the windows. The gunboats had nearly completed their circle.

"They've laid down a minefield, as you've undoubtedly already guessed. But as far as our pinpoint sonar can tell, they've set the mines at twelve feet. Their gunboats can pass right over the mines, but your vessel cannot."

"So what?" I shouted. "We have wounded men aboard, we want out of here."

"I know, Carter, I know. But you're going to have to hang on a little longer."

"How much longer?"

"The President has been advised. He's gone to the U.N. You people have to hang on."

I lowered the handset for a moment and stared out the window at the open sea. Somewhere out there was a minefield through which we could not pass. Farther out was a U.S. nuclear submarine whose captain was offering us platitudes. And five hundred miles away was Luzon in the Philippines. Freedom.

I raised the handset.

". . . you've got to understand," the submarine commander was saying.

"I've got to understand what, Captain?" I said.

"Goddammit, Carter, your President has ordered this. You and your people *will not* create a fuss. Do you understand what I'm saying to you."

"Bullshit, Captain," I snapped. I was tired and fed up now.

"Bullshit nothing, Carter. We'll get you and your people out of there, but it has to be our way.

Do you understand what I'm saying? Hanoi is listening to this conversation. They understand. Do you?"

Again I lowered the handset. What the hell was he saying to me? Hausmann and Sondra were watching me, mystified expressions on their faces. They had heard only my half of the conversation. They could not know what the submarine commander had told me.

I raised the handset.

"All right, captain, what do you want us to do?"

Wilson seemed relieved, "Stop right now and drop anchor."

"That all?"

"Stay right there, Carter. We'll get you out of this."

"How long?" I asked.

There was another hesitation. "What?"

"I said, how long? What's the timetable? How long are we going to have to stay here at anchor? The Paris peace talks took more than a year. We can't hold out that long."

"No one is asking you to hold out that long. Just a day or two. Forty-eight hours at the most."

"Forty-eight or seventy-two?" I asked.

"Seventy-two hours," Wilson said.

"Three days. That's it, Captain. After that moment, we leave."

"Carter . . ." the submarine captain protested. I cut him off.

"Three days, Captain, and then we head out. If it means sinking this vessel, with a loss of all hands and passengers, then so be it." I put the handset down and turned to the others who were staring at me.

"What the hell was that all about?" Hausmann snapped.

"We'd better get this ship stopped and anchors out. We're going to be here for a bit," I said.

Hausmann was clearly mystified, but he gave the order to the helmsman who complied, then got on the ship's intercom and ordered his crew to put out the bow anchor.

When he was finished, I got on the intercom. "This is Carter on the bridge. I want all squad leaders in the crews' mess on the double. All squad leaders in the crews' mess at once."

"What's going on, Nick?" Sondra asked when I was finished. "Who was in on the radio?"

"I'll explain everything in the crews' mess," I said and I turned to Hausmann. "How about your crew? How much do they know about what's going on here, and will they follow you?"

"They know about as much as I do, and yes they'll follow me. They're loyal."

"You'd better have your officers at the meeting as well."

Hausmann nodded.

"Go ahead down to the crews' mess," I said to Sondra. "I have something I have to do first. I'll be just a minute or two."

Hausmann gave me an odd look, but then I stepped off the bridge and hurried down to the main deck where most of the POWs still lined the rails.

A number of them gathered around me near the bow. They all wanted to know what was going on, why we had stopped.

"I'm going to explain it to your squad leaders, and they'll pass it on, but for now we're going to have to remain at anchor here. But you're going to have to keep a sharp watch on the gunboats. There's a possibility they might try something, especially tonight after it gets dark."

They were all watching me.

"If anything approaches this ship, and I do mean anything, I want you all to open fire immediately. I don't want anything within a hundred yards of us. Clear?"

They all nodded.

"All right then, I want you to pass the word on. We'll set up a schedule later today so that you can get some rest in shifts."

"Mr. Carter," one of the men said.

"Yes?"

"We *are* going to get out of here, aren't we, sir?"

"You're damned right we are. We haven't come this far to get stopped out here." I looked at them all. "And that is a promise."

THIRTEEN

Colonel Powell, his leg bandaged, was waiting in the crews' mess along with six of his officers. Captain Hausmann, his first officer and chief engineer were also there, along with Sondra. They all had intensely worried looks on their faces.

Sondra poured me a cup of coffee, and after I had taken a sip of it and had lit myself a cigarette, I began.

"As some of you already know, the Vietnamese have laid a minefield around us, making it impossible for us to continue—for the moment. I've told our people up on deck to be on the watch for approaching gunboats, and to repel with force any attempt to board this ship."

"Do you think that's what they're going to do, Nick?" Powell asked.

"I don't know. But it's a possibility we're going to have to guard against. When we're finished here, I suggest that you and your officers organize some kind of a schedule. Most of those men up there are practically asleep on their feet."

"We'll get on it as soon as we're done here," Powell said. "But what can we do to get ourselves out of here?"

"The U.S. nuclear submarine *Barracuda* is parked and submerged about eight miles to the southwest of our present position."

Everyone perked up. Hausmann and his officers seemed thunderstruck.

"I have been in contact with the submarine's commander who assures me that the President has been made aware of our situation out here. But— and this is a big but—they want to try and gain our release through diplomatic means, before we try any further force."

"How long, Nick?" Sondra asked. "How long are we supposed to wait out here?"

"Seventy-two hours."

She shook her head. "There's barely enough food, and certainly not enough water for that length of time. And then if they do release us, we'd not have enough to make it all the way to Luzon."

I was afraid of that. "We go on rationing immediately then."

A heavy silence descended upon the room then, until Powell spoke up.

"What happens at the end of three days, if negotiations have not produced any results?"

"Then we fight our way out."

"With the help of the submarine?"

"I can't answer that one, Gary. But I would assume that they would not allow us to be sunk. In any event we'd probably need their help in clearing a path through the minefield and holding the gunboats at bay."

"Meanwhile we sit here, low on food and water, eleven of my people wounded, four dead; sit here and rot."

"Those orders have come directly from the President. We'll do it his way for the next three days. After that, we'll play it by ear."

I turned to Powell's radio operator. "Phil, I want you to get up to the radio room and help Captain Hausmann's man monitor the Vietnamese frequencies. I want to know what they're saying. Might give us some clues."

"Yes, sir," Phil said.

"Any questions?" I asked.

"It's supposed to rain again tonight. I'll have my people put out some tarps. We should be able to catch some fresh water," Hausmann said.

"It'll help," I said. "Anything else?"

There was nothing.

"All right, let's get to it then."

Powell, Hausmann and Sondra remained behind, as the others got up and shuffled out. When everyone else was gone, Powell came over and perched on the edge of the table.

"They're taking this to the U.N., I suppose," he said.

"That's what I was told."

Powell nodded. "And I'm sure what's happening out here is being kept a secret."

"For now it will have to be that way," I said. "No one wants this to escalate into a shooting war."

"It won't happen in three days, you do know that, don't you?"

"You're probably right, Gary, but I gave them my word. We'll sit tight here for three days. After that, we're leaving."

"I hope so," Powell said thoughtfully. He got to his feet again. "But you know, Nick, I don't think any of this is going to work out so easily. I think we're going to be here a lot longer than three days."

He turned and left.

Hausmann put his coffee cup down and got to his feet with a heavy expression on his face. "When this is all over with, my crew and I will not be able to return home."

"I'm sorry, Captain, but I'll make sure that you and your people are taken care of."

"Yes," he said, shaking his head. He turned and left.

"What do you think, Sondra?" I asked. She and I were the only ones left in the crews' mess.

"I don't know. Hawk arranged this. Or at least set things in motion. But everyone is so gun-shy about another war here, that they're going to be overly cautious."

"Yeah," I said, stubbing out my cigarette. "Powell is right. This *isn't* going to be so easy."

Hausmann's steward assigned me a tiny cabin on the officers' deck two levels below the bridge. I went there immediately after the meeting. I took a hot seawater shower, then climbed into the narrow bunk where I fell asleep instantly.

I had left word with Phil up in the radio room to call me if anything happened, and Sondra had promised to wake me no later than midnight.

If the Vietnamese were going to make any move against us, I figured it would probably happen sometime after then. It would be the darkest part of the night, and we would be the least alert.

This was the first bed I had slept on in what seemed like years, and, I slept so soundly and dreamlessly it was almost as if I had been drugged.

I had no idea what time it was when I became aware that I was not alone in my room. I opened my eyes, but could not see a thing it was so dark in the tiny cabin.

"Nick?" Sondra's voice broke the silence. "Are you awake?"

"Yes," I said softly. "How long have you been here?"

"A couple of hours."

I raised my left arm so that I could see the luminous dial on my watch. It was a few minutes after eleven.

"Nothing has happened? There has been no communication?"

"Nothing," she said. "We've got lookouts posted all around the ship. We can see the gunboats out there constantly on the move, but they've come no closer."

"Did you get any sleep?"

"A couple of hours," she said, her voice small.

"Sondra?"

"Yes, Nick?"

"This will all work out," I said.

"I'm frightened."

I reached for my cigarettes and matches. When the match flared, I could see Sondra sitting across the room from me. She was wearing a bathrobe.

"You shouldn't have come," I said. "You're a damned good operations officer, but you are not a field operative."

"I wanted to be here, to help," she said. I could hear a rustle of cloth, and then movement.

She took the cigarette from my hand, stubbed it out in the ashtray, then climbed in the narrow cot with me. She was nude.

"I'm frightened, Nick," she said again. She was shivering. "Hold me, please hold me."

Slowly then, I kissed her lips, her neck and the nipples of her breasts which quickly became erect. Her breathing quickened as she rolled over on her back, pulling me on top of her.

"Make love to me, Nick. I need you."

We made love then, gently and deliberately at first, but then with a rising passion as we lost ourselves in each other.

I remembered at the end of our lovemaking that I had forgotten to call her fiancé back in Washington before we had left, but it didn't seem to matter much now.

We lay in each other's arms then, saying nothing, until midnight.

"I have to get up now," I said. "Why don't you stay here and sleep for awhile."

"Come back to me, Nick," she said sleepily.

"I will," I said. I got up, took another saltwater shower, then got dressed. By the time I was finished, and ready to leave, Sondra was sound asleep.

I pulled the covers up around her neck, kissed her on the nose, and then went out into the corridor and up the companionway to the bridge.

Hausmann's first officer, Rudi Schmidt, was the only one on the bridge, and he spun around, startled when I came in.

"Good evening, Mr. Carter," he said when he recovered. He had been standing at the windows looking through a set of binoculars.

"Didn't mean to startle you," I said, coming across to him.

"I'm a little jumpy, sir."

"We all are," I said. "Anything happening out there?"

"Same routine all night," Schmidt said. "They just keep circling. Every now and then, one breaks off and returns to the harbor. To refuel, I suppose. And perhaps get a fresh crew."

I could see the lights of the gunboats moving across the horizon and out to sea. In the other direction, however, the lights of Haiphong seemed close enough so that I could reach out and touch them.

I wondered what was happening there, and in Hanoi, and back home in Washington, and at the U.N. in New York.

"Two more days," I said.

"I hope so, sir," Schmidt said.

I left the bridge, went back down the companionway to the main deck level and stepped outside.

Some of the men were spread out along the rail from the bow to the stern. They looked my way.

"Good evening, Mr. Carter," the one nearest me said softly.

"How are things going out here?" I asked stepping up to the rail and peering over the edge down to the dark sea.

"Just fine, sir."

"I want you people to keep a sharp look out from now until dawn."

"The gunboats are still a long ways off."

"Right, and they'll probably stay that way. But meanwhile, when you're paying such close attention to the pretty lights, half the Vietnamese navy could be sneaking over here aboard rubber rafts."

He looked over the rail, then back at me, and grinned. "You're right, sir," he said. "We never thought of it. I'll spread the word."

"Do that," I said, and I moved off and went back into the main corridor, down the aft companionway and into the sickbay, where the doctor and the medics Sondra had brought along were doing what they could for our wounded.

Everyone was asleep down there, and I left without waking anyone, making my way back up to the officers' mess. I got myself a cup of coffee and then went back up to the bridge.

Schmidt heard me coming this time and wasn't so startled.

"Nothing has changed, sir," he said when I came in.

I nodded. "I don't think anything will, if we can get through this night."

"Sir?"

"Hanoi monitored my talk with the sub, and if they don't do anything tonight, I think they'll wait until the three days are up before they make any kind of a move."

"Then what, sir?" the young officer asked.

I shrugged. "Your guess is as good as mine," I said. "But it won't be pleasant, nor will it matter. If something hasn't happened by then, we're going to make our move."

The young officer didn't say a thing. Instead he turned and stared out the window.

Three days, I thought. A nearly impossible long time considering what the POWs had already gone through, and yet a nearly impossible short time considering what would have to be accomplished in the U.N.

Nothing happened that night, and the next

morning broke clear and very hot. No more rain
had fallen in the night, and the long-range forecasts
we were picking up from the Vietnamese
meteorological stations called for clear skies with
little or no chance for further rain for the next five
days.

By early afternoon of the first day, it was evident
that the POWs would not be able to maintain the
schedule that Powell had made out for them. They
were already weakened by their long captivity, and
the hot weather was sapping their strength even
further. Combined with the fact that we were all on
strict water and food rations, we had to cut back
on the number of lookouts we posted.

The second evening was a repeat of the first, except for the weather. Our first evening aboard had
been reasonably cool, with a pleasant breeze and at
least the chance of rain. But the second evening
was extremely hot and muggy, a haze in the air
making the distant lights of Haiphong seem to
shimmer.

And the POWs began to suffer. At first it was
just an isolated one or two of them falling with heat
prostration, but then more and more of them were
down with serious dehydration, dysentery, chills
and vomiting.

At one point, late in the afternoon of the second
day, the Italian doctor Sondra had hired for this
mission threw up his hands in frustration.

"These men are dying and there isn't a damn
thing I can do for them."

"What would it take to help them?" I asked.

The doctor, a short, very thin man, drew himself
up to his full height and looked me directly in the

eye. "Give this insanity up, Mr. Carter. Now. Before it is too late. These people need water, proper food, and release from the constant tension they've been under."

I nodded. "You're right, Doctor. And I wish I could give them that. But do you honestly believe that if we did give ourselves up they would receive any better treatment at the hands of the Vietnamese?"

The doctor said nothing.

"Have you talked to any of these people? Do you understand what they have gone through for the last ten years or more?"

"I understand," the doctor finally said. "I will do what I can, but do not expect miracles."

"No one does, Doctor. Believe me, no one does."

That night clouds came in from the southwest, and for a few hours we were all convinced that it would rain. Captain Hausmann's men put out tarps and buckets to catch any rain that might fall, but by two in the morning the clouds had dispersed, the moon had come out, and the thick haze had settled in, along with the heavy humidity and an infestation of bothersome flies.

We were giving it until noon of the third day, and moving into that dawn, I could sense that the POWs and the crew would not consider an extension.

Twice without any luck I had tried to raise the *Barracuda,* nor had our radioman been able to come up with anything of use or interest to us.

The Vietnamese military channels were strangely silent. It was made doubly odd by the fact that the

Laotians had attacked the border near Muong Va just a few nights earlier. But still, there was nothing on any of the channels.

I was up on the bridge the morning of the third day, when Phil called me down to the radio room.

Captain Hausmann was asleep on his feet in front of the windows, and the helmsman was sitting with his feet up at the navigational table when I dragged myself off the bridge and down the companionway to the small radio shack.

Phil, looking like death warmed over, was the only one in the tiny room that was crammed with ancient-looking equipment.

When I came in, he looked up dully at me and nodded. "Mr. Carter," he said.

"What have you got for us, Phil?" I asked, sitting down heavily next to him.

The air seemed so thick and hot that it was difficult even to breathe. My tongue seemed thick and my stomach rumbled.

"I've been listening to the foreign broadcast stations," he said.

"What about the military channels?"

"Listen to me, sir. There's been nothing about us on any of the foreign stations. Not BBC or CBC, not the European stations, not Radio Free Europe, or even Radio Moscow. Nothing."

"Of course not," I said, looking at him.

"Don't you see, sir, that if anything is going to be done for us in the U.N., it's going to take strong world opinion to accomplish it?"

Suddenly I saw what he was driving at. It came to me all at once.

"They're going to have to let everyone know

what is happening here . . ." the radio man was saying.

"What kind of transmitting equipment have you got here?" I interrupted him.

At first he didn't hear me, or didn't quite understand what I was asking, because he continued on about world opinion, but then he stopped.

"Sir?"

"What transmitters have we got here?"

He looked at the equipment in front of him. "VHF marine bands, single sideband radio-telephone . . ."

I cut him off again. "What about an emergency channel? Something that would transmit for a long distance that a lot of people could hear?"

"Single sideband," he said.

"Get it ready," I said.

"Sir?"

"Get your equipment ready, Phil. I'm going on the air in a little while and broadcast a message. We're going to get that worldwide publicity you were talking about."

Suddenly he realized what I was getting at, and he perked up. "Yes, sir," he snapped.

"Get ahold of Colonel Powell, Captain Hausmann and Sondra Kinderman. Tell them to meet me on the bridge on the double," I shouted over my shoulder as I hurried out the door, down the corridor and back up the companionway.

Hausmann was still on the bridge when I burst through the hatch, and he spun around.

"Tell your engineering section to fire up the diesels. Right now! And get the anchor up, we've got to be ready to move at a moment's notice."

"What?" Hausmann sputtered.

"Do as I say, Captain, I'll explain it just as soon as Powell and Sondra get up here."

FOURTEEN

The Vietnamese knew we had not brought any provisions with us when we fought our way aboard the *Karpitz* three days ago. And there was little doubt that when the ship was docked in port, they had inspected it. They had to know that we were now dangerously short of food and water.

We waited on the bridge for Colonel Powell to return with the list of every POW's name and hometown. He and his officers had responded to my request without question, which was just as well.

Staring out now at the gunboats circling us in the distance, I wondered what they would say when they knew what I was going to try.

But we had no choice any longer. The Vietnamese knew they would only have to stall negotiations for a few more days, and by then we would be so weak over here, that they could take us with little or no force.

The ship's intercom buzzed and Captain Hausmann picked it up. "Yes, he's here," he said. He held the handset out to me.

I took it from him. "Carter."

"Mr. Carter, this is the radio room. I've got a

clear frequency on the single sideband transmitter just above the amateur fifteen-meter band."

"Good job, Phil," I said. "Can you patch it up here so that I can transmit from the bridge?"

"Sure thing," he said. "Say the word and I'll set it up."

"Give me about five minutes and we'll be ready."

"I'm not going anywhere this morning," he said.

I hung up and a couple of minutes later Powell came in out of breath. He handed me some sheets of paper.

"I included our dead on this list as well," he said.

I looked over the names and shook my head. There were twelve dead now. Eleven had died of wounds during the fight to get aboard. The twelfth had died yesterday of some unknown sickness that had raged through his body.

The ship's diesels were throbbing on idle far below in the engine room, and the anchor had been raised, causing us to drift slowly back toward the harbor entrance three miles away.

Hausmann stood by the helm, Powell was right next to me, and Sondra stood, leaning against the bulkhead near the portside windows. They were all looking at me. All waiting for me to give them the magic formula that would get us out of here.

"You all understand our problem with food and water," I began. They all nodded. "And you also must understand that negotiations for our release will not be completed by noon today."

"So we're stuck out here," Powell said bitterly. "We'll all starve to death."

"If we remain here," I said.

"We can't get out," Hausmann snapped. "They've

got us boxed in with the minefield."

"In every direction except back into port," I said.

"Never . . ." Powell sputtered, but I held him off.

"Hear me out, Gary. I've got an idea, and as crazy and dangerous as it's going to sound to you, I think it just might work."

"Anything," Hausmann said. "We just can't stay here."

"That's the first point," I said. "The second point is that the *Barracuda* won't be able to help us either, which leaves us on our own." I glanced out the windows toward the distant gunboats. "Nothing can move through the minefields," I said. "Not us to get out, and not the *Barracuda* to get in."

"Except for the gunboats," Hausmann said. "They're shallow enough craft so that they go right over them."

"Exactly," I said, turning back.

Sondra was the first to understand what I was suggesting, and her eyes went wide. "You can't be serious," she said.

I nodded.

"What the hell are you talking about?" Powell demanded.

Then Hausmann got it, and he glanced out at the gunboats. "You mean to get us all aboard one of these gunboats, somehow, and then get the hell through the minefield?"

"Something like that," I said.

"How? They're constantly on the move. We can't get close to them with this ship, and even if we did, we'd never be able to get aboard."

"How many officers and crew do you suppose

one of them carry?" I asked.

Hausmann shrugged. "With the gunners, probably a dozen."

"Out here on maneuvers. How about in port, tied up to the quay or anchored within the breakwater?"

"That depends," Hausmann said. "They might all remain aboard, but on watches. There would be perhaps only three or four men awake at any given time during the night."

"That's what I thought," I said. "We're going back into the harbor and tie up at the docks."

"They'll just take us," Powell said. His face was turning red.

"We'll hold them off if need be. In any event, before we move back into the harbor, we'll make it clear why we're going back."

"And why's that?" Powell asked.

"For food and water, of course. We're going to go along wholeheartedly with the negotiation process. We're going to make it easier for everyone concerned. For the Vietnamese who want their concessions, which they won't get if we starve to death out here, and for our own government that does not want to start a shooting war out here."

Powell was having trouble with this. "Okay," he said. "So we steam back into the harbor and tie up at the dock. What's to prevent the Vietnamese from simply not giving us food and water, and then in a day or two, waltzing aboard and taking us? We'd be right back where we started from. My people won't go for that."

I held up the list of names. "This is our guarantee, Gary. This and an open radio channel that your radioman has rigged up. A lot of people, worldwide, are going to hear what I've got to say in just a couple of minutes. Once the word gets out that there are American POWs aboard this ship in Haiphong harbor, the Vietnamese will have to co-operate to keep us alive."

Still Powell was shaking his head. "Then we be-come hostages. Our government would have to ne-gotiate in a crisis situation. They can't do that. As long as we're out here free and on our own, the advantage is ours."

"You're not listening, Gary," I said patiently. "We're going back into Haiphong harbor, but we're not going to stay there for very long."

"Then how . . ."

"We're going to steal a gunboat tonight. When we have it, everyone is going to swim across and get on board, and then this ship is going to be started up, pointed straight for the harbor exit, and let go. Only there won't be anyone on board by then."

"In the confusion, we may be able to slip out of the harbor and make a run for the *Barracuda*," Sondra said.

Powell was looking from her to me and back again. "You're crazy," he said. He looked out at the distant gunboats again. "But there is no other way, is there?"

"None that I can think of," I said.

Powell seemed to think for a long time, until finally he nodded. "Let's do it then." He grinned. "The sonofabitches are in for the surprise of their lives."

When we had the radio link patched up to the bridge, and I was about to send my message outlining our situation here and then read a list of the names and hometowns of the POWs aboard, Powell stepped in.

"Let me do it, Nick," he said.

I didn't know if he was up to it emotionally.

"My wife, Becky, is out there. If everything else fails and if anyone happens to record our message, I want her at least to have a chance to hear my voice."

"They will, Gary, there's no doubt about it. We're going to be broadcasting on a well-monitored frequency." I handed him the list.

Powell looked it over, then took the handset from me, perched on the captain's chair, and began.

"This is United States Air Force Colonel Gary Stewart Powell, speaking from the German freighter *Karpitz* three miles offshore from the North Vietnamese port city of Haiphong.

"Along with more than one hundred and forty men, women and officers, I have been held as an illegal prisoner of war by the Vietnamese government for more than ten years."

Sondra was crying, and Powell's eyes were moist.

"If anyone is listening, if anyone can hear this message, we need your help."

The ship-to-ship radio buzzed angrily, and Hausmann answered it as Powell outlined the history of his capture and subsequent imprisonment.

"It's Wilson aboard the *Barracuda*," Hausmann said softly.

I took the phone. "Carter," I said.

"Carter, you sonofabitch, what the hell do you think you're doing?" Captain Wilson shouted.

"Doing, Captain?" I said. "Starving to death out here."

"You listen to me . . ."

"No, you listen to me, sir," I broke in. "We're out of food and water. We have twelve dead and another eight or nine wounded, as well as a number down with dehydration or dysentery. Even if we were released at noon, we would not be able to make it to Luzon."

"So what the hell do you think you'll accomplish by that broadcast?"

"We're going back into the port, where within a few hours I expect to be supplied with food, water and medicines. The Red Cross has a unit in Haiphong, or at least one up in Hanoi."

"That's it?" Wilson said. "That's all you're going to do?"

"That's it, Captain," I lied. "We need food and water and protection from recapture by the Vietnamese until your negotiations for our release can be completed."

"The President's going to be mad as hell. He wanted this all done in secret."

"The President may be mad, Captain, but we are dying out here. Please don't try to jam our frequency."

There was a silence on the air for a long moment. We both knew that the Vietnamese were monitoring our conversation.

"I wouldn't jam your signals if I could, Carter," he said. "Good luck to you."

"Thank you, sir," I said and I hung up and turned back to Powell who was still speaking.

"At noon, local time, we will be moving the *Karpitz* back into Haiphong harbor, where we will tie up at the main docks. I am broadcasting this so that everyone will know where we are, and what is happening to us. We will not be recaptured—alive. We will not suffer again the illegal imprisonment we have been subjected to for these long years."

Powell looked around at us, and I nodded for him to continue.

He turned back to the handset. "I will read now a list of the men and women with me. Adams, Francis P., captain United States Air Force, from Savannah, Georgia. Albright, Donald J., staff sargeant, United States Air Force, Duluth, Minnesota . . ."

Slowly then, Powell went through the list: name, rank and hometown. Several times he had to stop to compose himself, but each time he refused to allow any of us to continue for him.

Already, I was sure, the first preliminary news stories were flashing around the world over the wires of the Associated Press, United Press International, Reuters, and dozens of other news services.

Television programs in hundreds of cities were being interrupted to bring the announcement that something very extraordinary was happening in the Gulf of Tonkin a few miles off shore from Haiphong.

Analysts in a dozen governments were working out the possible ramifications to their own security and positions.

And the Vietnamese government at Hanoi had to be doing a slow burn. But it was too late for them.

I stepped off the bridge and looked down at the main deck. Powell's radio message was being piped throughout the ship, and the rails were lined with the POWs who had the strength to climb up from their makeshift quarters.

All of them were armed. A few seemed angry, ready for a fight, but most of them just stared east across the sea. The direction toward the Philippines and freedom.

Sondra joined me outside on the narrow bridge deck.

"A lot of those men won't be able to make it aboard the gunboat," she said.

"Then we'll carry them, or bring them across in a rubber raft," I said without looking up.

"And if it doesn't work, Nick?" she asked. "I mean if it's impossible for us to actually get control of a gunboat without being stopped?"

"Then the negotiations will continue. Meanwhile they'll have food and water. They won't starve to death."

"Will we ever get out of this, Nick?" she said.

I turned to her and smiled as I took her in my arms. "Of course we will," I said. "I've been in a hell of a lot worse situations than this one."

Powell finished around ten A.M., and after a very short silence, the POWs throughout the ship began cheering. We were all in this together, they were saying to their senior officer. And they would all see it to the end, together.

For the next two hours, Hausmann and his crew made the ship ready to move back into the harbor while Sondra and the medics helped the weaker POWs get cleaned up and ready for action.

"Tonight we move," I told Powell and his officers in the crews' mess.

"Won't they be expecting us to try something?" one of the officers asked.

"I don't think so. They're convinced that we're already half dead out here. They'll expect that we'll wait now for food and water so that we can build up our strength."

"Meanwhile, all they have to do is drug the water, and it would be over. No fuss no muss."

"Another reason we try tonight," I said.

We had gone over my plan in every detail for the past hour or so. And although there were holes in it large enough to drive a truck, it was all we had.

"Any questions, then?" I asked.

"Do we allow an inspection?" Powell asked.

"If they insist on it. But when they come aboard they'll find most of our people in bed, apparently too weak to move."

"How about force, Mr. Carter?" one of the officers asked. "What happens if they try to take the ship."

"We repel them with everything we've got," I said sitting forward. "I don't think there's any question in anyone's mind what would happen to us if we were recaptured."

There were no answers, but we all knew what would happen. We'd be swallowed up and not heard from again until our government gave the Vietnamese every single thing they wanted. There would be no escaping the second time.

"Any other questions?"

There were none, and I got to my feet. "Get your people to their posts. The most critical moment will come when we actually dock. Have your people ready for it. Everyone else remains below."

"We'll give 'em hell, Mr. Carter," one of the officers said.

I grinned. "I'll hold you to that," I said.

Powell and I went back up to the bridge where Hausmann, his first officer and the helmsman were waiting for us.

"Everyone ready below?" Hausmann asked.

"We're ready," I said. "Radio the Haiphong Port Control and tell them we're coming in, and then let's get started."

"All ahead slow, and bring the bow around to two-six-five," Hausmann gave the order.

"All ahead slow, two-six-five, sir," the helmsman said, and we began to move, turning back toward the harbor entrance as Hausmann got on the ship-to-shore frequency.

He spoke briefly in Vietnamese, and when he hung up he was grinning. "We're to dock at the same place we left."

"That's considerate," I said. "For them to hold our parking place."

The gunboats, which had been circling, moved in closer providing us with an escort, funneling us directly toward the entrance in the breakwater.

The Soviet destroyers were still anchored in their same spots, but many of the other boats that had been in the harbor three days ago had been moved.

Within a half an hour, we had passed the breakwater entrance, and Hausmann carefully maneuvered the ship past the Soviet ships, easing alongside the dock where we had fought our way from the trucks to the ship.

There were at least a hundred heavily-armed soldiers on the dock, along with dozens of motor vehicles and a large mound of supplies, which I took to be provisions. They had moved fast.

Hausmann's men flipped the docking lines over the bow and stern to Vietnamese dock workers who tied us up, and then the ship's engines were shut down.

A gangway was wheeled over from one of the warehouses and put in place.

Hausmann, Powell and I all stepped out onto the bridge deck as two Vietnamese officers and a dozen soldiers started up the gangway.

"Only the officers, no soldiers," Powell called down in Vietnamese.

The contingent stopped and looked up at us.

"We could take this ship in less than five minutes," one of the officers shouted up in English.

"You are invited to try," I shouted. At that moment forty armed POWs who had been hiding behind the rails, stood up so that they were in plain view.

The Vietnamese stepped back reflexively.

"Do not create an incident here today," I shouted down. "We will defend this vessel to the last man."

The officers said something to each other, then the one who was the spokesman looked back up at us.

"There is food and water here for you and your people. You may come down and get it."

"Your people, unarmed, will bring the supplies aboard immediately. In addition, within twenty-four hours we will want to see the International Red Cross representatives. Is that clear?"

Again the officers conferred.

"We would like to come up and speak with your

captain and your senior POW."

"Request denied," I shouted. "Remove yourself from this vessel now, and send the supplies aboard."

The officer stared up at us for a long moment. "As you wish," he finally called up. "We mean you no harm."

The officers and soldiers backed down off the ramp, and a few minutes later a dozen unarmed dockworkers began bringing the supplies aboard for us. They laid them on the deck and then quickly retreated.

"Round one," I said.

Powell was sweating, his knuckles white where he gripped his weapon.

"Don't blow it now, Gary. We're too close. We've just won the first round, and by this time tomorrow we'll be damned near Luzon where I'll buy you a steak with all the trimmings, and a barrel of beer."

Powell looked at me and blinked. "You're on."

FIFTEEN

It took about ten minutes for all the provisions the Vietnamese were supplying us to be brought aboard, and when the dockworkers had finally left the ship, I leaned over the guard rail on the bridge deck.

"Get those supplies below on the double," I shouted, making sure that the soldiers on the dock could hear me. "I want the strongest men fed and given water first, then you can distribute meals to those in the sick bays."

One of the deck hatches clanged open, and a half a dozen POWs dragged themselves to the supplies and began hauling them belowdecks.

It could have been a comedy except for the fact that most of the men below were not feigning weakness. But the show had the desired effect on the soldiers on the docks.

They were convinced now that taking this ship would present few if any problems by tomorrow at this time.

"Keep a sharp watch," I called down to the armed POWs along the rails, and I went back inside.

Hausmann was standing away from the windows, out of sight of anyone on the docks, and he was grinning broadly. "They believed you," he said.

"We'll see what happens in the next few minutes. If they don't try anything right away, I don't think they will until tomorrow. They'll probably be under the guise of the Red Cross."

I buzzed for the dispensary. The doctor Sondra had brought along answered.

"It's on its way," I said. "Let me know as soon as possible."

"Right," the doctor said, and he hung up.

I buzzed next for the radio room. Phil answered.

"What are you picking up from the military channels?" I asked.

"Not much. They're maintaining a fairly strict radio silence. Their important traffic is encrypted."

"How about the civilian channels?"

Phil laughed. "We're headline news everywhere, and I do mean everywhere."

"Even Tass?"

"Especially the Russians. They claim we're a strike force here to take over Haiphong in an attempt to cripple Vietnam's major port city."

"What else?"

"The Pope has said a prayer for us, and the President says he is doing everything within his power to gain our release."

All standard comments. I was reasonably certain that Hawk suspected I was up to something; he knew me well enough. But I wondered if anyone else had any inkling of what we were going to try to do.

"Anything happening yet on the docks?" I asked Powell.

"Not yet," he said as I joined him at the windows.

"What next?" Hausmann asked.

"We wait and see what the doctor has to say," I said. "And we watch to make sure they don't try anything down there."

Several more armored vehicles had been brought out onto the dock. Sandbag barricades had been set up at either end of the long, concrete quay.

A pair of the gunboats had been tied up in front of us, and two more were tied up aft. Eight others were idling slowly in circles a few hundred yards away. They would not let us simply slip our lines and sail away this time.

The day was becoming very hot. The bridge was like an oven, and we were all sweating heavily, but the POWs along the rail were out in the hot sun, and I knew they had to be suffering. Yet we could not let them stand down, not yet. Not until we were absolutely sure what the Vietnamese were planning to do.

I was just about to call down to the dispensary, when the ship's intercom buzzed, and I picked up the handset.

"Bridge," I snapped.

"The water is drugged, and the food is all dehydrated. We can't use any of it," the doctor said.

"What kind of drug? Anything we can circumvent?"

"It's some compound of amyl nitrate as far as I can tell with the equipment I've got on board."

"Would it be fatal?"

"Hard to tell, but I doubt it. We'd all be out for twenty-four hours or more, though, if we drank so much as a tablespoon of water."

"All right, get rid of it all then. And pass out the rest of our food and water."

"What?" the doctor protested. "What the hell will we do tomorrow?"

"We're going to be long gone from here by tomorrow, Doctor," I said. "And after you've passed out what provisions we have left, get our wounded ready to be moved."

"When are we going?"

"Tonight, after midnight."

"We'll be ready," the doctor said, and I was about to hang up when Powell grabbed the handset from me.

"Doctor? This is Colonel Powell. Have you got enough airtight body bags for our dead?" Powell blinked back some tears. "Good. I want all twelve bodies put in the bags, and then I want the bags filled with air before they're sealed. Do you understand?" He blinked again. "That's it exactly, Doctor. Thank you." He hung up the phone and looked defensively at us. "They're coming with us when we leave," he said softly.

"No one is being left behind, Gary," I said.

"I'm going to rotate the men," he said. "Midnight's the hour?"

"Midnight," I said, and he left.

For a long moment I stared at the hatch through which he had left, then I sighed deeply. The next twelve hours or so would tell the tale. We were either going to succeed in grand style or fail spectacularly.

But that, I told myself, had been for foregone conclusion from the beginning of this assignment.

"Your people are finished below?" I asked Captain Hausmann.

"They were finished before we hit the break-water."

I tried to think of whether or not I had forgotten anything, but I was tired and hungry and fuzzy headed.

"I'm going to get some rest now."

"I'll be here awhile," Hausmann said. "We'll wake you if anything happens."

I left the bridge and trudged wearily down the companionway to the radio room where Phil and the *Karpitz's* radioman were listening to Radio Free Europe, which was playing music.

They both looked up when I came in.

"Midnight," I said to Phil.

"I'll be ready, sir," he said.

"Get some rest first."

"Yes, sir." he said.

I left the radio room and went down to the next level to my cabin, where I flopped down on my bunk and lit myself a cigarette.

There was a very good chance that come midnight, my actions could cause the death of every one of the POWs, Hausmann's crew, and Sondra. It wasn't a very comforting thought, yet I could think of no other way out of our present situation.

I had a brief, guilty thought about Father Lars dying out there on the minefield between Laos and Vietnam, but then my thoughts turned to Father Josef and his sister Therese.

By now they should have already been across China and down somewhere in Laos. I hoped that they were all right. Possibly the Laotian attack on the Vietnamese border had kept the Laotians busy enough so that their interior patrols were weak. I wanted to see Father Josef again, and to have that drink of cognac with him in Tirlemont.

I stubbed out my cigarette, rolled over and finally went to sleep, the sweat pouring off my body in the hot, humid Vietnamese afternoon.

I dreamt. The images I saw were confused, ranging from AXE headquarters in Washington, D.C., to the monastery in Tirlemont.

Sondra was standing over me, shaking me by the shoulder. "Nick?" she called from a long way off. "Nick?"

I turned over and opened my eyes, reality rushing at me. "Sondra?"

"It's midnight," she said, and I realized that I was no longer dreaming. I was awake.

I sat up and swung my legs over the edge of the bed. My head was pounding. It was still very hot and muggy.

"I brought you some water," she said, holding a small cup out in front of my face.

I took it from her and drank the tepid ounce or two of water, then set the cup aside.

"Is everyone else ready to go?" I asked.

"They're assembling down on B deck, at the cut."

I got up, went across the room to the tiny bathroom, and splashed some lukewarm seawater on my face. Back in my cabin, Sondra had turned on the lights, and I quickly checked my Luger and my stiletto in its chamois sheath.

"I want to come with you," Sondra blurted.

I looked up and shook my head. "No."

"I don't want to be left here," she said, her voice rising.

I crossed the room to her and took her shoulders

in my hands. "Hang on just a little longer, Sondra. We'll get out of this."

"I left my apartment unlocked," she said almost hysterically.

"Sondra? Listen to me."

"I didn't call my mother," she screamed.

I slapped her in the face, and she suddenly collapsed, sobbing against my shoulder.

I held her for a long time then, as she cried herself out. Her body seemed so frail, and it was hot and flushed.

When we parted I looked into her eyes. "How much water did everyone get on this last ration."

"An ounce or two," she said.

There had been twice that much in what she had given me.

"Did you get your ration?" I asked.

"I . . ." she sputtered. "Yes . . . I . . ." She looked away.

"Christ," I said. She had given me her water. "I won't leave you here, I promise you Sondra. But you have to believe me."

"I do," she said wide eyed.

I kissed her. "Get everyone else ready for the transfer. We're not going to have a lot of time. Colonel Powell knows what to do, and Captain Hausmann will be getting the ship ready. You're going to have to help with the wounded."

She was nodding.

"We'll get out of this."

She nodded again.

I released her and without looking back went out the door, down the corridor, and headed belowdecks down the companionway.

On our way back from our anchorage outside

the harbor, Captain Hausmann's crew had torched a large hole in the plates just above the water line, about admidships, leaving only two small tabs of steel holding the plate in place.

The hole was located in a small crawl space just above the engine room, and when I worked my way back to it, off the engine-room companionway, I could see several small flashlights bobbing in the darkness.

"Carter?" someone said.

"It's me," I replied. "Everyone here and ready?"

"Yes, sir."

"Then douse those lights. We're going to need our night vision."

The lights went out, and for several moments I could see spots in front of my eyes, but gradually I could see the line cut out of the plates. Hausmann's crew was supposed to have come down here during the confusion on the docks and hacksaw the two holding tabs away.

"Are we through? Is the plate loose?"

"Yes, sir," one of the six men who would be going with me said.

"How about the gunboats?"

"One passed about two minutes ago. It's clear now," someone else said.

"We have all our equipment?"

"Yes, sir."

"Let's do it, then," I said.

Two men put their shoulders against the plate and shoved, once, twice and on the third time the thick steel plate popped loose, swung outwards, and then splashed into the water less than three feet below.

Instantly I could smell the seawater and the city

of Haiphong, and I could see the lights of the other boats out in the harbor, including the Soviet destroyer out by the breakwater.

"Let's go," I said, and the six POWs slipped out of the hole, one by one, making little or no noise as they entered the water.

I was the last in the bath-warm water, and within minutes we had swum the length of the *Karpitz* and were treading water near the bow. The stern of the gunship tied up at the dock in front of us was dark, and we could see no one on the fantail.

The bridge of the ship, however, was lit in a soft red glow. And from time to time we could see someone moving around up there.

To the left, up on the dock, we could see four soldiers sitting around an overturned crate playing cards and talking. None of them were looking this way, and we could hear them laughing.

I motioned for the others to move out, and I began swimming slowly in a smooth breaststroke, careful not to break water and make any noise.

Within a minute or so, I had made it to the stern of the gunboat, and I held up there as the others joined me.

On the bow of the *Karpitz* less than thirty yards away, I could see one of our POWs leaning against the rail, smoking a cigarette.

He looked directly down at me and nodded, then flipped his cigarette out into the water.

One of the men with me edged a little away from the others as he uncoiled a bent steel bar, around which had been wrapped several layers of cloth and a length of rope.

Swinging it awkwardly as he tread water, he

flipped the homemade grappling hook up over the low rail of the gunboat.

It landed with a dull thud, and one of the POWs in the water, who was in a position so that he could see up on the docks, held his arm up out of the water for several long seconds. It was our signal that we had been heard.

Finally he brought his arm down. Everything was back to normal.

I slipped my stiletto out of its sheath on my left forearm, put it between my teeth, then swam over to the rope, tested it, and quickly scrambled up the four feet or so to the gunboat's rail.

The grappling hook had caught under the lip of the rail. No one was on the fantail as I slipped quietly aboard.

Within less than one minute the others were aboard. Silently I motioned for Phil, our radio-man, and one of the other POWs to come with me while the others slipped below to take care of the off-duty crew.

From what we could see, it seemed as if the on-duty crew members were all on the bridge. They certainly were expecting no trouble from us, and combined with the fact that there were guards on the dock, their vigilance was lax.

As soon as the others had disappeared below, we hurried forward, came up behind the rocket launcher, and scrambled up the ladder to the bridge deck.

The bridge hatch was on the sea side, so we were hidden from view from the dock. Unless there was some commotion here, we would not be discovered.

I carefully peered over the lower edge of the window. There were three men on the bridge, all of them sitting down, their feet up, smoking.

I ducked down again. Phil and the other man had their knives out, and using sign language, I indicated to them that there were three men inside and what their positions were.

Phil and the other POW nodded. I took a deep breath, let it out slowly, then turned the latch on the door, counted to three and shoved it open.

I was on my man before he realized what was happening, drawing my stiletto sharply across his neck, severing his jugular veins and windpipe.

Phil took care of his man, but the third Vietnamese had leaped to the window and started to shout before the other POW brought him down.

Then it was quiet for a moment.

I grabbed the cap off my downed man and tossed it over to Phil who put it on. I motioned for him to stand up.

He did so slowly, then stiffened, and finally waved before he turned away and walked nonchalantly across the bridge so that he was no longer visible from the dock.

"They heard something," he said. "They were looking up here."

I edged to the window and slowly peered over the sill. The four soldiers below on the dock were just settling back to their cards, evidently satisfied that nothing was wrong.

Quickly, Phil and the other POW dressed in the dead men's uniforms, and we settled down to wait.

Within a couple of minutes there was a soft beeping from the walkie-talkie Phil had carried over wrapped in plastic.

He held it up to his mouth and ear. "Yes?"

A moment later he looked up, smiled and gave me the thumbs up. "The boat is ours."

I glanced down at the dock again. The soldiers were still playing cards. Both ways along the dock, other soldiers were lounging around as well, waiting for the morning when they would attack the *Karpitz*. Only we were going to be long gone by then.

"Signal for the others to start coming over," I said softly. "Then get this boat ready to move out."

"Yes, sir," Phil said, and he spoke into the walkie-talkie as I left the bridge. Keeping low, I went down to the main deck and worked my way aft to the fantail.

A couple of the POWs from below had come on deck, and together we waited for the others to begin coming over from the *Karpitz*.

We didn't have to wait long. Within two minutes, I could see several heads bobbing in the water alongside the larger ship, and they began moving across to us.

Within twenty minutes we had pulled twenty POWs aboard, but then we had to stop for a few minutes as two of the patrolling gunboats passed.

When they were gone we resumed the transfer, pulling the POWs up over the rail, and hustling them immediately belowdecks.

Sondra and the medical crew were among the last to come over. She kissed me on the cheek, and then went below as a few more came across.

Finally it was just Captain Hausmann, his first officer and chief engineer left aboard the *Karpitz*. The mooring lines had been cut almost completely through so that the slightest nudge would break them.

We were finally ready.

I made my way back up to the bridge. Nothing had changed below on the docks. No alarms had been sounded.

"Now," I said to Phil, who raised the walkie-talkie to his lips.

"Now," he said.

A few seconds later, the *Karpitz's* diesels suddenly came to life, and the big ship began easing away from the dock, her mooring lines falling away.

Almost immediately sirens began sounding throughout the port, and soldiers came running from every direction along the dock.

The radio aboard our gunboat began pinging wildly, and the POWs dressed in Vietnamese uniforms jumped up in plain view and started the engines, while other POWs from below, who had dressed in Vietnamese uniforms, appeared on deck to man the guns and the rocket launchers.

The *Karpitz* continued to move ponderously away from the dock, her diesels winding up to full revolutions, as gunfire began to come from the docks.

Once the ship had swung her bow around so that it was pointed directly at the breakwater exit across the harbor, she stopped turning.

Meanwhile our crew had slipped the gunboat's lines, and we moved away from the dock, coming up within a few feet of the moving bulk of the cargo ship.

We let the bigger ship get slightly ahead of us, as we watched three figures leaping from the tiny hole in the side near the water line.

The *Karpitz* was moving faster now, and we let her get even farther ahead of us while the other gunboats began moving in, their spotlights flashing back and forth.

In the confusion, we were easily able to pick up Hausmann and his two officers, and then we headed out in hot pursuit of the fleeing vessel that was accelerating even faster now on a course set by her autopilot.

Like the other gunboats, we fired several shells across the *Karpitz's* bow before we all passed through the breakwater into the open sea.

Then I nodded toward the helmsman, who suddenly slammed the throttles forward full speed.

The big gunboat fairly leaped forward, heading straight out to sea, sirens wailing, shells bursting around the *Karpitz*, and the other gunboats concentrating their efforts on the cargo ship.

Phil was on the radio talking fast with Wilson over on the *Barracuda*, and within two or three minutes we all realized that we had made it.

Even if the other gunboats suddenly came after us, they no longer would be able to catch up before we made it to the protection of our sub.

The cheering began below on the decks as our communications radio pinged for us to come back. The shouts of pure joy were overwhelming.

EPILOGUE

Someone was pounding on the door to my cottage on the base at Luzon, and I came slowly awake.

Sondra lay curled up asleep next to me on the wide bed, and she didn't move as I got up, threw on my robe, and went to the door and opened it.

It was morning. The sun shone from a perfectly blue sky, and birds were singing in the lush foliage in the park across the narrow street.

A young signal corpsman was standing on the stoop. "Commander Carter, a message for you, sir," he said, handing me a flimsy. "I think it's in code, sir," he said.

From Hawk, I wondered? I opened the message and quickly read it. Suddenly I was laughing out loud, the signal corpsman looking at me as if I was a crazy man.

"Sir?" he said. "Is everything all right?"

"Everything is fine, son," I said. "Just fine." I closed the door.

Sondra was sitting up in bed, her breasts lovely in the morning light.

"What's wrong, Nick?" she asked, alarmed.

"Nothing," I said, still laughing. "Not a damn

thing, except that we're going to celebrate today."

"What?" Sondra questioned, as I let the message flimsy fall to the floor, and went to her.

"We're going to celebrate," I shouted. "Champagne, caviar, the works."

I stopped a moment by the bed, turned and looked back at the message. I was going to celebrate here today, but I had another celebration to go to in a couple of days. This one would be in Tirlemont.

The message had been sent from Brussels. It was clear, very concise, and very, very welcome.

            TO: NICK CARTER
                 LUZON, PHILIPPINES.

            WHAT THE HELL TOOK YOU SO LONG
            STOP VERY FINE COGNAC AWAITING
            YOUR ARRIVAL TIRLEMONT STOP END
            OF MESSAGE.

                                    SIGNED
                            FATHER JOSEF

DON'T MISS THE NEXT NEW
NICK CARTER SPY THRILLER

RETREAT FOR DEATH

It was late, sometime after two in the morning, when I woke up, aware for some reason that we were no longer alone in the apartment.

Pat was cradled in my left arm, her lovely breasts crushed against my chest, her long legs intertwined with mine.

We had come back to her apartment early, had finished a bottle of very good Dom Perignon, and then had gone to bed where we had made slow, gentle love to the strains of Tchaikovsky's violin concerto.

We had fallen asleep in each other's arms, able at least for that moment to forget the danger we were both in, able for that moment to forget the terrible image of her brother leaping to his death from the eightieth floor of the World Trade Center in New York.

Now they were back to finish what they had begun, and lying here nude, I felt more vulnerable than I have ever felt.

Slowly, so as to make absolutely no noise, I moved myself away from Pat, disengaging my legs from hers and easing my arm from beneath her head.

Whoever was with us in the apartment was somewhere directly across the room from the bed. I could hear breathing and some other, soft, scratching noise.

Every muscle in my body tensed as I made ready to fling back the covers and leap up, but at that moment a blinding light flashed in the corner, the sudden sharp odor of sulphur wafted across the room to me, and something very sharp pierced my neck just above my right shoulder.

"Nick?" Pat screamed as I leaped out of the bed, stumbling as the covers twisted in my legs.

A heavy, numb feeling began to rapidly spread from my neck, down my shoulder, through my right side as I struggled to get up.

Flames were rising up from a pile of clothing and paper in the corner, as I managed somehow to get unsteadily to my feet.

Two men were at the door, both of them tall and husky.

"He's up," one of them shouted, his voice coming from a long way off.

"Never mind, Sid, let's get out of here," the other one said.

Sid. The name and the face swam in my fuzzy

brain as I took several shaky steps forward, finally collapsing near the chair where I had tossed my clothes and my Luger in its shoulder holster.

I was fumbling for it when something slammed into my face, snapping my head back, and I fell over.

The man named Sid was standing over me, his face garishly illuminated in the flames that were rapidly filling the apartment.

"Die, pig," he said, and he laughed . . .

—From RETREAT FOR DEATH
A New Nick Carter Spy Thriller
From Ace Charter in August